WILSON®
just words®

Student
Challenge Book

WILSON®

Wilson works®

Wilson Language Training Corporation

www.wilsonlanguage.com

Name: _____

WILSON® Just Words® Student Challenge Book

Item # JWSCHB

ISBN # 978-1-56778-401-5

PUBLISHED BY:

Wilson Language Training Corporation
47 Old Webster Road
Oxford, MA 01540
United States of America

(800) 899-8454

www.wilsonlanguage.com

Printed in the U.S.A.

January 2022

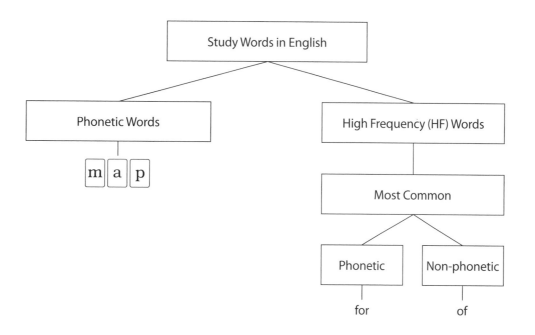

Units 1-3 Check

1 _____	9 _____	17 _____
2 _____	10 _____	18 _____
3 _____	11 _____	19 _____
4 _____	12 _____	20 _____
5 _____	13 _____	21 _____
6 _____	14 _____	22 _____
7 _____	15 _____	23 _____
8 _____	16 _____	24 _____

Units 4-7 Check

1 _____	12 _____	23 _____
2 _____	13 _____	24 _____
3 _____	14 _____	25 _____
4 _____	15 _____	26 _____
5 _____	16 _____	27 _____
6 _____	17 _____	28 _____
7 _____	18 _____	29 _____
8 _____	19 _____	30 _____
9 _____	20 _____	31 _____
10 _____	21 _____	32 _____
11 _____	22 _____	

Units 8-10 Check

1 _____	9 _____	17 _____
2 _____	10 _____	18 _____
3 _____	11 _____	19 _____
4 _____	12 _____	20 _____
5 _____	13 _____	21 _____
6 _____	14 _____	22 _____
7 _____	15 _____	23 _____
8 _____	16 _____	24 _____

Units 11-14 Check

1 _____

2 _____

3 _____

4 _____

5 _____

6 _____

7 _____

8 _____

9 _____

10 _____

11 _____

12 _____

13 _____

14 _____

15 _____

16 _____

17 _____

18 _____

19 _____

20 _____

21 _____

22 _____

23 _____

24 _____

25 _____

26 _____

27 _____

28 _____

29 _____

30 _____

31 _____

32 _____

Brief History of English Language

1.	2.
8,000 years ago	Logograms
3.	**4.**
Some Chinese Logograms	5,000 years ago: Egyptian Hieroglyphics
5.	**6.**
Today: English Alphabet	26 Letters: More than 250,000 words

Tap out sounds. Read the word. Write the letter(s) for each sound in the boxes.

math	=	m	a	th	gap	=	
mash	=				hub	=	
lad	=				sash	=	
shack	=				dim	=	
chat	=				shock	=	
cash	=				tax	=	
jab	=				dock	=	
such	=				sag	=	
thick	=				lush	=	
path	=				rash	=	
posh	=				sob	=	
sub	=				pun	=	
chug	=				thud	=	
vat	=				chuck	=	
nag	=				fib	=	

PHRASE PRACTICE

was a **quiz**	**nab** the **sub**
the **pup hid**	**did** they **mix**
in the **hip**	**did** Bob **nap**
Ted is **sad**	**mop** the **vat**
tub was **wet**	**pug** is a **pet**

they **cut sod**	a **mob** is **big**
quip is a **pun**	**quit** the **job**
Ed did **run**	**log** on **top**
hem the **bib**	in the **den**
wig was **hip**	was the **hub**

PHRASE PRACTICE

from the **dish**

in the **back**

rush on **deck**

shop was **posh**

lack of fun

hush the **mob**

then they **shop**

rock is **thin**

are not **thick**

have **such** fun

on the **neck**

such a **rush**

they are **sick**

cod is **fish**

have **much luck**

tip the **jack**

on the **path**

have the **lock**

a big **thud**

in a **shock**

MARK UP BOLD WORDS

Underline digraphs.

di<u>sh</u>

Did Jack mop the deck?

Did Jack mop the deck?

1   Ted hit his chin on the log.

Ted hit his chin on the log.

2   Ed had to hush the mob.

Ed had to hush the mob.

3   They did not whip up that fish dish.

They did not whip up that fish dish.

4   Did they jog on the path?

Did they jog on the path?

5   Bob got a pet dog from his Dad.

Bob got a pet dog from his Dad.

PHRASES FOR CHARTING

from the dish

was not hot

quip is a pun

have a wish

lash to deck

are in back

they are sick

was a quiz

quit the job

have this lock

with a thud

did Bob nap

is not quick

tub was wet

dish of fish

pug is a pet

1 DETERMINE SCORE

→	TOTAL WORDS READ
−	ERRORS
=	WORDS READ CORRECTLY

2 CHART PROGRESS

GRAPH YOUR SCORE ON THE "MY PROGRESS" CHART FOR THIS UNIT

Student Name: _____ Unit# _____ Test Date: _____

SOUNDS

1 _____ 2 _____ 3 _____

WORDS

1 _____ 6 _____

2 _____ 7 _____

3 _____ 8 _____

4 _____ 9 _____

5 _____ 10 _____

PHRASES

1 _____ 3 _____

2 _____ 4 _____

SENTENCES

1 _____

_____

2 _____

_____

UNIT SCORES

SOUNDS _____ /3   MARKING _____ /2 (☐ All elements of task 1 ☐ All elements of task 2)

PHONETIC WORDS _____ /20   CAPITALIZATION _____ /2 (☐ Sentence 1 ☐ Sentence 2)

HIGH FREQUENCY WORDS _____ /10   PUNCTUATION _____ /2 (☐ Sentence 1 ☐ Sentence 2)

LEGIBILITY _____ /1 (☐ All writing is legible)

Name _____

1. _____

2. _____

3. _____

4. _____

5. _____

6. _____

7. _____

8. _____

9. _____

10. _____

11. _____

12. _____

13. _____

14. _____

15. _____

1. (have) a <u>wish</u>

2. (from) the <u>shed</u>

3. (what) a <u>blast</u>

4. <u>strap</u> (your) bag

5. (where) he <u>slept</u>

6. (why) it <u>spilled</u>

7. (how) to <u>extend</u>

8. (write) the <u>contract</u>

9. had (been) <u>neglectful</u>

10. (place) in <u>Wisconsin</u>

11. (would) be <u>brave</u>

12. (move) a <u>franchise</u>

13. had (two) <u>reptiles</u>

14. is (too) <u>disruptive</u>

15. (once) was <u>inactive</u>

(HF Words)   = _____ / 15
+ <u>Phonetic Words</u> = _____ / 15
   Total   = _____ / 30

Progress Check Unit 2

Tap out the word. Segment the word by writing the letter(s) for each sound in the boxes.

risk = | r | i | s | k |

split = | | | | | |

stack = | | | | |

brisk = | | | | | |

trim = | | | | |

scrub = | | | | | |

tusk = | | | | |

brunch = | | | | | |

crack = | | | | |

drench = | | | | | |

thump = | | | | |

thrust = | | | | | |

shred = | | | | |

plump = | | | | | |

bench = | | | | |

swift = | | | | | |

shrub = | | | | |

stump = | | | | | |

whisk = | | | | |

strap = | | | | | |

Cross out any nonsense word that isn't a closed syllable. Mark all closed syllables. Read the nonsense closed syllable words.

rĭmp	bloid	um	stoit
~~sti~~	fro	quo	glain
thisk	upt	plent	fleme
floup	ouf	shelt	skish
spem	loum	hilk	chelp
ist	fime	flet	ple
che	twa	vount	osk
trub	twog	freth	plon

Mark the closed syllables and the exceptions (**ind**, **ild**, **old**, **olt**, **ost**) to the closed syllable rule. Read the words below.

bōld	bind	host	kind
chŏmp	told	blind	find
wild	child	post	mind
most	hold	colt	sold
tint	gasp	wild	mist
jolt	find	pond	land

PHRASE PRACTICE

just for luck

lost the **flock**

had a **hunch**

squid do **swim**

mend the **vest**

got the **hint**

trap to set

do not **squish**

a **pinch** of **mint**

trim one **twig**

lump of **slush**

his **grip** was **limp**

do that **task**

must have **lost**

trim the **shrub**

crack the **bench**

one **last spin**

held his **block**

snug in the **nest**

the **best** for **last**

MARK UP BOLD WORDS

Underline blends and digraph blends with separate lines for each sound.

<u>bl</u> <u>i</u> <u>mp</u>, <u>sh</u> <u>r</u> <u>e</u> d

PHRASE PRACTICE

you **struck gold**

hold the **frog**

colt was **blind**

trench was **cold**

scrod for **brunch**

the **sprint** was **swift**

twist your **belt**

where they **slept**

felt them **stomp**

your **craft** will **drift**

spend your **cash**

you **blend well**

squint in the **smog**

trust your **gut**

flush the **pump**

sold your **script**

one **strut** has **rust**

sprig of **mint**

the **blimp** is **plump**

they were **told**

MARK UP BOLD WORDS

Mark words as closed or closed exceptions.

Did Jack mop the deck?

1　Did the kids stop to rest at the pond?

2　They were told that the smog is bad.

3　The last class skit was the best one.

4　Mom will help you get set for the quiz.

5　The kids got the hint and sat on the bench.

6　The dog is cold but the pup is not.

7　The child did not spend all his cash.

8　Did you find the lost colt?

9　All the kids must help dad scrub the deck.

10　Do not trip on that big old stump.

PHRASES FOR CHARTING

one stick did snap

held one flag

sold your mask

trap the frog

must have lost

they were told

do that task

where is scrap

stop to rest

you struck gold

you spend well

a gust of wind

was a find

strum the drum

do not squish

just for luck

1 DETERMINE SCORE

→	TOTAL WORDS READ
–	ERRORS
=	WORDS READ CORRECTLY

2 CHART PROGRESS

GRAPH YOUR SCORE ON THE "MY PROGRESS" CHART FOR THIS UNIT

WILSON® Just Words®

Unit Test

Student Name: _____   Unit# _____   Test Date: _____

SOUNDS

1 _____   2 _____   3 _____

WORDS

1 _____   6 _____

2 _____   7 _____

3 _____   8 _____

4 _____   9 _____

5 _____   10 _____

PHRASES

1 _____   3 _____

2 _____   4 _____

SENTENCES

1 _____

_____

2 _____

_____

UNIT SCORES

SOUNDS _____ /3   MARKING _____ /2 (☐ All elements of task 1 ☐ All elements of task 2)

PHONETIC WORDS _____ /20   CAPITALIZATION _____ /2 (☐ Sentence 1 ☐ Sentence 2)

HIGH FREQUENCY WORDS _____ /10   PUNCTUATION _____ /2 (☐ Sentence 1 ☐ Sentence 2)

LEGIBILITY _____ /1 (☐ All writing is legible)

Name _____

1. _____

2. _____

3. _____

4. _____

5. _____

6. _____

7. _____

8. _____

9. _____

10. _____

11. _____

12. _____

13. _____

14. _____

15. _____

HF Words = _____ / 15
+ Phonetic Words = _____ / 15
Total = _____ / 30

1. did (they) fix

2. (was) not sick

3. (do) not sniff

4. (where) he slept

5. (who) was told

6. (what) he flunked

7. (which) was toxic

8. they (were) absent

9. (why) he invested

10. (would) not astonish

11. it was fantastic (also)

12. (want) a quote

13. (often) did explode

14. much (more) intensive

15. (could) not strike

Progress Check Unit 3

Add bonus letters to words that need them. Star bonus letters. Box all welded sounds.

dill ★	milk	club	nip
c⬚all ★	stal	that	quiz
vat	hal	sped	shel
pas	fuz	mis	cros
gap	ches	buf	shut
dres	swift	staf	cob
rap	tal	gulf	snif
con	bal	flos	quil
thug	golf	mif	dul
mes	shop	whip	stres
bel	muf	huf	flos
mal	bas	bras	buf
shred	chug	draft	fal
cuf	skul	shack	slot

Read the words. Box the "welded" sounds with **ng** or **nk** letter combinations (**ing**, etc.).

shr|ink|	lung	plant	strong
plug	skunk	grind	brand
stink	swing	slug	chill
grunt	fang	gang	trunk
draft	brag	blog	stuck
string	black	yank	blank
tank	mink	twig	bring
chunk	hung	flung	cliff

Write the words with boxed sounds on the lines below.

ng words   **nk** words

_____   _____

_____   _____

_____   _____

_____   _____

_____   _____

_____   _____

_____   _____

PHRASE PRACTICE

what to **stress**	clump of **tall grass**
tell us why	which old **stuff**
cross your **boss**	when you **stall**
which kind of **jazz**	they do **spell**
dress for the **mall**	have your **fill**

call his **bluff**	**press** your **cuff**
spill the **fizz**	why quiz the **staff**
toss which **stuff**	one **small skull**
what a **thrill**	when to **smell**
buff to a **gloss**	what to **drill**

MARK UP BOLD WORDS

Box welded sounds. Star bonus letters.

f[all]★   cuff★

PHRASE PRACTICE

who in the **band**

with some **brand**

staff **plan** well

who had a **cramp**

some **bank scam**

shift the **lamp**

how to **stand**

stamp on the **ant**

fall in **sand**

slam the ball

what a **strong** smell

how it **shrunk**

how to **thank** you

come **ring** the bell

king was **stung**

what to **drink**

slang from a **punk**

when to **bunk**

stink of **skunk**

ping-pong champ

MARK UP BOLD WORDS

Box welded sounds.

b⟨an⟩d

Math Test Pangs

Jess had much to do and the task was big. When the bell rang, she had to be set for the next class. She had a big math test, and she felt that she did not get all of it. On her last quiz, she got stuck and had to get some help. Jess did not stress, but she did ask kids to stop the chat. They did not mind and went into the hall. Jess had to think. She had to cram for the test. She had a list and did one thing, then the next. When the bell rang, she felt a quick pang in her gut, but she did not shrink from the task at hand. Jess was all set for the math test.

In the math class, Jess got the test. She held it and then went blank. Then she had to stop and think. At last she got a pen. She had to trust what she did to get set for this test. She did her best and in the end, she did not do a bad job at all. In fact, she got stuck on just one spot. As she left the class, Jess was glad that the math test went so well.

PHRASES FOR CHARTING

who to thank

king was stung

which to stress

fill in the blank

when to toss

come with Frank

how to stand

rip the dress

cross which path

what a thrill

they do spell

which did shrink

one small skull

why not sing

press your cuff

which kind of jazz

1 DETERMINE SCORE

→ TOTAL WORDS READ	
− ERRORS	
= WORDS READ CORRECTLY	

2 CHART PROGRESS

GRAPH YOUR SCORE ON THE "MY PROGRESS" CHART FOR THIS UNIT

WILSON® Just Words®

Student Name: _____ Unit# _____ Test Date: _____

SOUNDS

1 _____ 2 _____ 3 _____

WORDS

1 _____ 6 _____

2 _____ 7 _____

3 _____ 8 _____

4 _____ 9 _____

5 _____ 10 _____

PHRASES

1 _____ 3 _____

2 _____ 4 _____

SENTENCES

1 _____

_____

2 _____

_____

UNIT SCORES

SOUNDS	____ /3	MARKING	____ /2 (❑ All elements of task 1 ❑ All elements of task 2)
PHONETIC WORDS	____ /20	CAPITALIZATION	____ /2 (❑ Sentence 1 ❑ Sentence 2)
HIGH FREQUENCY WORDS	____ /10	PUNCTUATION	____ /2 (❑ Sentence 1 ❑ Sentence 2)
		LEGIBILITY	____ /1 (❑ All writing is legible)

Name _____

1. _____

2. _____

3. _____

4. _____

5. _____

6. _____

7. _____

8. _____

9. _____

10. _____

11. _____

12. _____

13. _____

14. _____

15. _____

1. (they) did <u>gab</u>

2. (have) a <u>sock</u>

3. he (was) <u>still</u>

4. (who) will <u>trust</u>

5. (do) the <u>most</u>

6. <u>cramped</u> (your) leg

7. had (some) <u>tonic</u>

8. (shall) not <u>disrupt</u>

9. (which) is <u>distracting</u>

10. (should) be <u>consistent</u>

11. (once) did <u>inhabit</u>

12. (put) the <u>blame</u>

13. (push) to <u>exhale</u>

14. (friend) was <u>inactive</u>

15. (use) the <u>slide</u>

(HF Words)   = _____ / 15
+ <u>Phonetic Words</u> = _____ / 15
   Total   = _____ / 30

Progress Check Unit 4

Read the word. "Scoop" baseword and circle suffix. Write the baseword and suffix.

		Baseword	+ Suffix			Baseword	+ Suffix
crashes	=	crash	+ es	brushes	=	_____	+ ___
shifts	=	_____	+ ___	swings	=	_____	+ ___
sprints	=	_____	+ ___	drafts	=	_____	+ ___
inches	=	_____	+ ___	squints	=	_____	+ ___
blesses	=	_____	+ ___	cuffs	=	_____	+ ___
skunks	=	_____	+ ___	crunches	=	_____	+ ___
splashes	=	_____	+ ___	blinds	=	_____	+ ___
grunts	=	_____	+ ___	stands	=	_____	+ ___
folds	=	_____	+ ___	shrinks	=	_____	+ ___
munches	=	_____	+ ___	presses	=	_____	+ ___
blinks	=	_____	+ ___	twists	=	_____	+ ___
quills	=	_____	+ ___	stresses	=	_____	+ ___

"Scoop" or underline the baseword and circle the suffix in each word below. Read the word. Mark the suffix with /**t**/, /**d**/, or /**ed**/ depending on the sound.

/t/ blink(ed)	rested	bonked
/d/ smell(ed)	punched	scripted
/ed/ insist(ed)	willed	stamped
passed	stalled	lumped
bonded	thrilled	puffed
dumped	shifted	trusted
stamped	clenched	swished
called	trashed	plucked
shocked	pinched	crunched
thanked	melted	skilled
quilted	winked	stocked
banged	filled	dashed
blocked	fluffed	listed
filmed	camped	blended

PHRASE PRACTICE

punches toward left

stops some **pranks**

drinks two **drops**

grabs two **blanks**

frogs also jump

drags toward us

thanks him too

also has **skills**

dunks for **fans**

trusts too much

also **fixes ramps**

two punk **bands**

stresses too long

also **smells** skunk

sends toward the west

have two **lungs**

your two **walls**

twigs from **trunks**

passes the ball

toward the **stands**

MARK UP BOLD WORDS

Underline the baseword and circle the suffix. For suffix -**s**, indicate sound of -**s** suffix (/**z**/ or /**s**/).

/**z**/   /**s**/
bug(s)   drop(s)

PHRASE PRACTICE

does stop **swelling**

pinching shall stop

two are **crossed**

telling some **fibs**

planted both **shrubs**

blended two together

holding classes together

spilled both **boxes**

scolded too fast

does too much **spending**

---

stocked both **kinds**

dresses are **shrinking**

which **holding** tank

where they **shifted**

falling toward the **benches**

drilled for black gold

all **lumped** together

does mind **dumping**

does some **squinting**

passed the lunch

MARK UP BOLD WORDS

Underline the baseword and circle the suffix.

<u>brush</u> (ing)

The "Big One"

Brad did not think that it was the best day for fishing, but still, he called Bill. They had the day off and Bill was glad to go with Brad. They were the two kids who did the most fishing, but they did not catch many fish. Both of them were together when Brad's dad got the "Big One". That was such a thrill. The fish was twenty inches long! Brad and Bill also wished to catch such a grand fish, but they had not had the luck yet.

On this day, Brad and Bill went toward that old spot on the pond. Brad was standing up in the small boat to send out the fishing line. Brad trusted that the boat would not tip, but it did. Bill blocked Brad's fall, but still he fell in the pond with his fishing rod. When he got back in the boat, he was a wet mess! At the end of the day, Bill had one sunfish, but that was it. They were still glad to have had the day off and to spend it fishing together even if they didn't get a thing.

PHRASES FOR CHARTING

drifted toward the shrubs

also was shocked

does some sprinting

thanks him too

both were passed

melted it together

also squints

which was grinding

shall be billed

falling off the cliffs

jumped toward west

bosses too much

holding classes together

does not rest

both are drenched

drilled for black gold

1 DETERMINE SCORE

→ TOTAL WORDS READ	
− ERRORS	
= WORDS READ CORRECTLY	

2 CHART PROGRESS

GRAPH YOUR SCORE ON THE "MY PROGRESS" CHART FOR THIS UNIT

Student Name: _____ *Unit#* _____ *Test Date:* _____

SOUNDS

1 _____ 2 _____ 3 _____

WORDS

1 _____ 6 _____

2 _____ 7 _____

3 _____ 8 _____

4 _____ 9 _____

5 _____ 10 _____

PHRASES

1 _____ 3 _____

2 _____ 4 _____

SENTENCES

1 _____

_____

2 _____

_____

UNIT SCORES

SOUNDS _____ /3   MARKING _____ /2 (☐ All elements of task 1 ☐ All elements of task 2)

PHONETIC WORDS _____ /20   CAPITALIZATION _____ /2 (☐ Sentence 1 ☐ Sentence 2)

HIGH FREQUENCY WORDS _____ /10   PUNCTUATION _____ /2 (☐ Sentence 1 ☐ Sentence 2)

LEGIBILITY _____ /1 (☐ All writing is legible)

WILSON® Just Words®

Name _____

1. _____
2. _____
3. _____
4. _____
5. _____
6. _____
7. _____
8. _____
9. _____
10. _____
11. _____
12. _____
13. _____
14. _____
15. _____

HF Words   = _____ / 15
+ Phonetic Words   = _____ / 15
Total   = _____ / 30

1. (from) the <u>mix</u>
2. (do) not <u>rock</u>
3. (for) a <u>dress</u>
4. did (you) <u>spend</u>
5. (they) are <u>bold</u>
6. (were) not <u>stumped</u>
7. (who) did <u>panic</u>
8. (which) is <u>splendid</u>
9. (what) was <u>expected</u>
10. (once) was <u>magnetic</u>
11. (push) to <u>establish</u>
12. had (two) <u>stripes</u>
13. was an <u>athlete</u> (too)
14. (sure) was <u>expansive</u>
15. a <u>line</u> (above)

Progress Check Unit 5

Underline or "scoop" the two syllables. Mark the syllables with a **c** to indicate a closed syllable. Put a breve (˘) above the short vowels. Read the words.

mĭsfĭt c c	nutmeg	vanish	victim
magnet	goblin	mascot	public
summit	splendid	upset	sudden
expel	misfit	insist	cobweb
limit	rocket	topic	sonic
clinic	septic	relish	Dublin
jacket	bandit	enrich	habit
freshen	candid	hobnob	frantic

Nonsense Words

Read the nonsense words. Underline or "scoop" the two syllables. Mark the syllables with a **c** to indicate a closed syllable. Put a breve (˘) above the short vowels.

stĭpdĕx c c	stonmic	findid	hobnum
debish	jonlen	thabit	fampel
brenset	popmeg	shotlet	taltic
musfit	trabcot	tucket	azbim
stoblet	quislet	gussot	chibot
polit	famjan	pippet	nixib

Divide each word below into syllables. Read the word. Write the syllables on the lines.

gumdrop	= <u>gum</u> <u>drop</u>	Atlantic	= ___ ___ ___
express	= ___ ___	athletic	= ___ ___ ___
bobsled	= ___ ___	fantastic	= ___ ___ ___
conflict	= ___ ___	Wisconsin	= ___ ___ ___
slingshot	= ___ ___	discredit	= ___ ___ ___
handbag	= ___ ___	inhabit	= ___ ___ ___
wildcat	= ___ ___	inhibit	= ___ ___ ___
complex	= ___ ___	discontent	= ___ ___ ___
culprit	= ___ ___	consensus	= ___ ___ ___
humdrum	= ___ ___	astonish	= ___ ___ ___
enchant	= ___ ___	quintuplet	= ___ ___ ___
grandslam	= ___ ___	recommend	= ___ ___ ___
sandblast	= ___ ___	accomplish	= ___ ___ ___
kingdom	= ___ ___	volcanic	= ___ ___ ___

PHRASE PRACTICE

want some **catfish**   wants to **limit**

frolic too often   two **splendid** wings

block the front **exit**   **rustic** front hall

which snug **jacket**   **disrupt** the class

what a **splendid sunset**   find the **mascot**

---

insult his friend   **polish** Jill's **locket**

where **combat** was   shall **insist** often

will not **infest**   flung **himself** toward

septic tank in front   **napkin** for **picnic basket**

shock the **public**   often **finish** last

MARK UP BOLD WORDS

Underline or "scoop" multisyllabic words into syllables.

goldfish

PHRASE PRACTICE

---

put the **drumstick**   was not **complex**

did a **handstand**   **punishes** them together

pull in **goldfish**   **discredit** your friend

one **fantastic pumpkin**   **kingfish** are **frantic**

put in which **sandbox**   **children** who **tantrum**

---

friend in **Wisconsin**   **polishes** off **gumdrops**

disrupted the plan   **publishes indented** text

finished a full **drumstick**   **implanted** an **optic** lens

full of **chestnuts**   **inhabit** the **toxic** land

they have **blindfolds**   has **magnetic** pull

MARK UP BOLD WORDS

Underline or "scoop" multisyllabic words into syllables. If the word has a suffix, circle it.

pumpkin(s)

The Thrill of Camping

The Chezwick twins had both longed to go camping, but had not had much luck yet. The last attempt to camp with friends had ended with unexpected cold and a drenching, wet mess. This fall they wished to go on a camping trip to the West End Camp. In the spring, it was too wet there, but in the fall, the grass on the bank of the pond would not be drenched. Some of the kids objected. Both twins did not mind that the West End Camp was a bit rustic, but some of the other kids did mind that.

In the end, they would plan a camping trip to the West End Camp. The camp was in a spot that had many wild plants and shrubs. Some of the kids had a plan to sketch all the kinds of wild plants and then find them on the web when they got back from the trip. The twins and friends in the club had much planning to do. They had often wanted to put up a tent dwelling on the bank of the West End Pond. At last, they were going to camp together.

PHRASES FOR CHARTING

finishes the script

has magnetic pull

push that pumpkin

insisted too often

flung himself toward

full of goldfish

pocket is packed

will not disinfect

chipmunks are frantic

finishes the topic

polished all the desks

solid as rock

disrupted that friend

napkin for splendid lunch

win both contests

wants to limit

1 DETERMINE SCORE

→	TOTAL WORDS READ
–	ERRORS
=	WORDS READ CORRECTLY

2 CHART PROGRESS

GRAPH YOUR SCORE ON THE "MY PROGRESS" CHART FOR THIS UNIT

Student Name: _____ *Unit#* _____ *Test Date:* _____

SOUNDS

1 _____ 2 _____ 3 _____

WORDS

1 _____ 6 _____

2 _____ 7 _____

3 _____ 8 _____

4 _____ 9 _____

5 _____ 10 _____

PHRASES

1 _____ 3 _____

2 _____ 4 _____

SENTENCES

1 _____

_____

2 _____

_____

UNIT SCORES

SOUNDS _____ /3   MARKING _____ /2 (❑ All elements of task 1 ❑ All elements of task 2)

PHONETIC WORDS _____ /20   CAPITALIZATION _____ /2 (❑ Sentence 1 ❑ Sentence 2)

HIGH FREQUENCY WORDS _____ /10   PUNCTUATION _____ /2 (❑ Sentence 1 ❑ Sentence 2)

LEGIBILITY _____ /1 (❑ All writing is legible)

WILSON® Just Words®

Name _____

1. _____
2. _____
3. _____
4. _____
5. _____
6. _____
7. _____
8. _____
9. _____
10. _____
11. _____
12. _____
13. _____
14. _____
15. _____

1. (from) the gap
2. on (your) neck
3. spell (one) word
4. had (some) shrimp
5. (which) was sold
6. (who) was thrilled
7. (was) not frantic
8. (how) to insist
9. they (were) publishing
10. (would) be invalid
11. (friend) is athletic
12. (once) did shame
13. (use) the concrete
14. (both) are inexpensive
15. (does) not stroke

(HF Words)   = _____ / 15
+ Phonetic Words   = _____ / 15
   Total   = _____ / 30

Read the words. Underline the baseword and circle the **er** (noun-person) or **er** (comparative) suffixes.

<u>sing</u>(er)	golfer	planter	quicker
kinder	fonder	insulter	publisher
jumper	longer	drinker	taller
dweller	stronger	grunter	milder

Write the words with the -**er** suffix which indicate a person on the lines below.

er - "person who"

singer

_____   _____

_____   _____

_____   _____

_____   _____

_____

Write the words that use an -**er** suffix for comparison on the lines below. Change the words to greatest form by adding **est**.

er / est words (compare)

kinder → kindest

_____ → _____

_____ → _____

_____ → _____

_____ → _____

_____ → _____

_____ → _____

Read the baseword. Select a suffix from the box at the top of the column to add to the baseword to form a different word. Write the suffix and then the word on the lines provided.

Vowel Suffixes		
ed	ing	er
es	en	est

Consonant Suffixes		
ment	ness	ful
less	s	

bench + _es_ = _benches_

box + ____ = _____

wild + ____ = _____

dress + ____ = _____

spin + ____ = _____

wag + ____ = _____

shoplift + ____ = _____

publish + ____ = _____

thrill + ____ = _____

finish + ____ = _____

insist + ____ = _____

mild + ____ = _____

fix + ____ = _____

hum + ____ = _____

insult + ____ = _____

trust + ____ = _____

punish + ____ = _____

blink + ____ = _____

stress + ____ = _____

ship + ____ = _____

scrap + ____ = _____

disrupt + ____ = _____

run + ____ = _____

invest + ____ = _____

limit + ____ = _____

fond + ____ = _____

rest + ____ = _____

mascot + ____ = _____

napkin + ____ = _____

thank + ____ = _____

PHRASE PRACTICE

should get **stronger**

cold milk **drinker**

have been **quicker**

does hit **longest** ball

was **kindest** one

seller would call

were the **tallest**

been much **fonder**

could be a **bluffer**

wildest in the mall

---

smallest attic **dweller**

should come together

the best **golfer**

quickest to finish

could insult the **publisher**

would be a **planter**

the **jumper** fell

both **driller** and **sander**

both children are **taller**

has been the **mildest** one

MARK UP BOLD WORDS

Underline the baseword and circle the suffix.

stronger

PHRASE PRACTICE

had been most **restful**

once the **shipment**

there shall be **punishment**

toward the **embankment**

some **thankful** children

nabbed robber

often much **madness**

once a **wishful singer**

in their **establishment**

their **quickness** often **wins**

---

come into a **shopful**

running fast to finish

madness not too **restful**

who was once much **wilder**

their **handful** of **bags**

into **bigger boxes**

shipped there once

could have been **distrustful**

some **kindness** into it

from their **gruffness**

MARK UP BOLD WORDS

Underline the baseword and circle the suffix.

rest(ful)

The Bat House

Did you ever witness hundreds and hundreds of bats together? This is not the kind of bat you will find with a ball. This bat is a small mammal that is 3 to 4 inches long with wings. They can zip from their resting spot in seconds. They have thin wings which help them be fast.

There is one spot in the United States where you can see vast flapping of bat's wings at sunset when they rocket all at once to find insects and moths. How did all the bats get to this one spot? The bats were hanging in the stands of a tennis complex on a campus in Florida. They were a pest to the fans and the bad smell of the bat dropping was also a problem. Then the campus constructed a bat house to get the bats from the tennis complex. The bats went to that resting spot. You can find bats in all the lands on the planet, but if you visit this campus, you will be sure to see lots of them. At sunset, up to 100,000 bats all exit the bat house within ten minutes!

PHRASES FOR CHARTING

would be restful

been much flatter

child was selfish

could swim longest

should have grabbed

the limitless vastness

there was scrubbing

once had a shipment

toward the embankment

should clamp stronger

full of plumpness

shopful of pink dresses

quicken their step

once had kindness

tantrum was milder

their tallest drummer

Student Name: _____ *Unit#* _____ *Test Date:* _____

SOUNDS

1 _____ 2 _____ 3 _____

WORDS

1 _____ 6 _____

2 _____ 7 _____

3 _____ 8 _____

4 _____ 9 _____

5 _____ 10 _____

PHRASES

1 _____ 3 _____

2 _____ 4 _____

SENTENCES

1 _____

_____

2 _____

_____

UNIT SCORES

SOUNDS _____ /3 MARKING _____ /2 (☐ All elements of task 1 ☐ All elements of task 2)

PHONETIC WORDS _____ /20 CAPITALIZATION _____ /2 (☐ Sentence 1 ☐ Sentence 2)

HIGH FREQUENCY WORDS _____ /10 PUNCTUATION _____ /2 (☐ Sentence 1 ☐ Sentence 2)

LEGIBILITY _____ /1 (☐ All writing is legible)

Name _____

1. _____

2. _____

3. _____

4. _____

5. _____

6. _____

7. _____

8. _____

9. _____

10. _____

11. _____

12. _____

13. _____

14. _____

15. _____

HF Words = _____ / 15

+ Phonetic Words = _____ / 15

Total = _____ / 30

1. (do) not <u>quit</u>

2. (is) in <u>shock</u>

3. (have) the <u>drill</u>

4. (why) it <u>shrunk</u>

5. had (some) <u>mold</u>

6. (when) it <u>smelled</u>

7. (who) is <u>comic</u>

8. (you) will <u>disrupt</u>

9. (where) it <u>expanded</u>

10. (would) <u>inhabit</u>

11. (both) are <u>consistent</u>

12. (friend) did <u>scrape</u>

13. <u>invited</u> us (together)

14. (sure) was <u>disruptive</u>

15. (often) did <u>trade</u>

Progress Check Unit 7

Read the words below.

thrive	shade	shack	smog
scrape	split	graze	chill
swipe	draft	brake	draft
slot	shave	nose	sting
crane	shred	clinch	pose

List the closed syllables and mark the short vowels. List the **v-e** syllables and mark the long vowels.

closed syllables		**v-e** syllables	
slŏt c	___	thrīve v-e	___
___	___	___	___
___	___	___	___
___	___	___	___
___	___	___	___
___			

Nonsense Words

Underline or "scoop" the two syllables in each word. Read the nonsense words. Put a **c** under the syllable for closed or **v-e** for vowel-consonant-e. Mark the vowels.

căp sāte c v-e	vilmite	dispote	explobe
disfume	fretjome	laxtile	mentrabe
retnest	denflate	ligstruct	condrape

Add suffix to baseword. Mark the **v-e** syllable in the baseword. Add the **e** above if it was dropped from the baseword. Circle the suffix.

hope + less = h͞op̄e(less)
v-e

hope + ing = h͞op̄(ing)
e
v-e

hope + ed = _____

confuse + ing = _____

shave + er = _____

explode + ing = _____

chase + ed = _____

shame + ful = _____

complete + s = _____

complete + ing = _____

"Scoop" and mark the syllables in the baseword and circle the suffix in the words below. If a silent **e** was dropped from the baseword when the suffix was added, indicate the **e** above the word. Read the words.

sh͞am̄e(ful)
v-e

ĭnvĕst(ment)
c   c

e
t͞ap̄(ing)
v-e

thankless

embankment

stampeding

hoping

homeless

reptiles

insulted

lameness

insider

thankless

prideful

exploding

wildest

inflated

postponement

dresser

trusting

invested

active

disruptive

confusing

plumpness

cared

hopeful

enrichment

constructive

shamed

publishing

PHRASE PRACTICE

pull toward the **rope**

could **wipe** the **plate**

when **Jane** is done

your friend **spoke** often

shake some more

their friend **chose**

broke his **nose**

his pranks are **lame**

prune that **rose** more

where they will **pose**

---

sure to **chase**

done once too often

weld the **bike** together

vote more often

rule from your **throne**

use **stone** in front

when done with **these**

share more **time**

sure to come **home**

jumped into that **pile**

MARK UP BOLD WORDS

Mark the v-e syllables.

PHRASE PRACTICE

completes both **dives**

dislikes an **umpire**

flute was above **volume**

the old **reptiles**

some rules **expired**

inflating the raft

slide toward the **baseline**

move in the **springtime**

included five **olives**

shall write a **statement**

place **cakes inside**

into a **caveman costume**

move your **trombone**

above the **concrete**

the **entire grapevine**

give up **biking**

write the **objectives**

done in your **lifetime**

code is **confusing**

shamed by **mistake**

MARK UP BOLD WORDS

"Scoop" into syllables. If there is a suffix, circle it. Mark syllable types.

Limit Those Plastic Bags

It is common to use plastic bags, but they are a bad problem all over the globe. A plastic bag is made from a thin plastic film. They make a mess for the planet. Stores and shops put things in plastic shopping bags. Rubbish is often put in these bags too. These plastic bags are in landfills or dumps, which are the common sites for such trash.

It is a shame when these bags end up on the side of the road or in lakes and ponds. Just when you admire the landscape, you then witness the mess of the bags which litter it. If the fish think that they can dine on the bag, it can kill them. These bags can take up to 1,000 years to disintegrate!

In some places, there are bills passed to limit the use of plastic. Some are collecting cash from stores that use plastic bags, which has helped combat and cut back the problem. With rules such as these, it will help to save the wildlife and welfare of the planet. The bottom line is that plastic is not so fantastic.

PHRASES FOR CHARTING

1 DETERMINE SCORE

→ TOTAL WORDS READ
− ERRORS
= WORDS READ CORRECTLY

2 CHART PROGRESS

GRAPH YOUR SCORE ON THE "MY PROGRESS" CHART FOR THIS UNIT

must use care

trading in baseball

place cakes inside

give a dare

inspired to move

some more rules expired

slide toward homeplate

above those piles

disliked that reptile

inflating their tires

find costumes inside

sure does admire

write until sunrise

where they will pose

postpone both games

snake was distinctive

Student Name: _____ Unit# _____ *Test Date:* _____

SOUNDS

1 _____ 2 _____ 3 _____

WORDS

1 _____ 6 _____

2 _____ 7 _____

3 _____ 8 _____

4 _____ 9 _____

5 _____ 10 _____

PHRASES

1 _____ 3 _____

2 _____ 4 _____

SENTENCES

1 _____

_____

2 _____

_____

UNIT SCORES

SOUNDS	___ /3	MARKING	___ /2 (☐ All elements of task 1 ☐ All elements of task 2)
PHONETIC WORDS	___ /20	CAPITALIZATION	___ /2 (☐ Sentence 1 ☐ Sentence 2)
HIGH FREQUENCY WORDS	___ /10	PUNCTUATION	___ /2 (☐ Sentence 1 ☐ Sentence 2)
		LEGIBILITY	___ /1 (☐ All writing is legible)

Name _____

1. _____

2. _____

3. _____

4. _____

5. _____

6. _____

7. _____

8. _____

9. _____

10. _____

11. _____

12. _____

13. _____

14. _____

15. _____

1. (was) a <u>lad</u>

2. (they) did <u>wish</u>

3. (you) <u>trust</u> him

4. (where) it <u>sold</u>

5. <u>cross</u> (which) path

6. (come) and <u>stand</u>

7. was (also) <u>thrilled</u>

8. (does) some <u>sprinting</u>

9. (often) was <u>frantic</u>

10. the (front) <u>expanded</u>

11. a <u>magnetic</u> (pull)

12. (could) be <u>quicker</u>

13. <u>humming</u> (their) song

14. was <u>piled</u> (above)

15. (write) until <u>sunrise</u>

(HF Words)   = _____ / 15
+ <u>Phonetic Words</u>   = _____ / 15
   Total   = _____ / 30

"Scoop" baseword and circle the suffix. Also mark digraph, blends, bonus letters, and welded sounds.

---

blinding	shrinks	cuffless	spinned
stamped	kinder	wildest	prongs
reddish	shipment	branded	thankful

Cross out any nonsense word that does not contain a closed, closed exception, or v-e syllable. Mark all closed, closed exception and v-e syllables. Read the nonsense words that are marked.

---

frĕth	che	fleme	loum
vount	glain	scromp	sind
dāfe	lang	gry	stoit
scraff	chelp	leuth	drepe
brile	bine	ple	dold

Underline or "scoop" the word into syllables. Mark the syllables. Read the word.

---

frăntic	jacket	concrete	captive
clockwise	comic	misconduct	inhabit
postpone	diminish	pensive	entire

Write the word with the suffix on the line. Follow spelling rules as needed.

quick + ness = <u>quickness</u>   distrust + ful = _____

thin + est = _____   bask + ed = _____

line + ed = _____   wipe + er = _____

invite + ed = _____   home + less = _____

sad + en = _____   brave + est = _____

box + es = _____   confuse + ing = _____

embank + ment = _____   nab + ed = _____

Match the meaning and example to the root. Use your Student Notebook if needed.

Root	Meaning	Example
duct	<u>lead</u>	<u>conduct</u>
mit	_____	_____
fract	_____	_____
tract	_____	_____
scrib	_____	_____
struct	_____	_____
junct	_____	_____
tox	_____	_____
pend	_____	_____
spec	_____	_____

Meaning

join	break
hang	look
pull, drag	~~lead~~
send	poison
build	write

Example

tractor	transmit
scribble	suspend
fracture	inspect
toxic	juncture
~~conduct~~	construct

Student Name: _____   *Test Date:* _____

SOUNDS

1 _____   2 _____   3 _____

WORDS

1 _____   6 _____

2 _____   7 _____

3 _____   8 _____

4 _____   9 _____

5 _____   10 _____

PHRASES

1 _____   3 _____

2 _____   4 _____

SENTENCES

1 _____

_____

2 _____

_____

UNIT SCORES

SOUNDS	____ /3	MARKING	____ /2 (☐ All elements of task 1 ☐ All elements of task 2)
PHONETIC WORDS	____ /20	CAPITALIZATION	____ /2 (☐ Sentence 1 ☐ Sentence 2)
HIGH FREQUENCY WORDS	____ /10	PUNCTUATION	____ /2 (☐ Sentence 1 ☐ Sentence 2)
		LEGIBILITY	____ /1 (☐ All writing is legible)

For each nonsense syllable mark blends, digraphs, digraph blends, and welded sounds. Star any bonus letters. **(20 points)**

splosh   pr[ink]   bress⭑

strill   flinch   shrank   spran   snall

plung   blost   squiff   chind   thronk

"Scoop" baseword into syllables and circle any suffix. Mark the syllable types in the baseword.   **(40 points)**

trŏmbōng(s)
c   v-e

costumes   admire   tantrums   distinctive   include

conflicting   reptile   disrupted   postponement   finishes

goldfish   sandblasted   homesickness investment   homeless

Spell the /k/ sound in words below.   **(10 points)**

franti_c_

publi___   shrin___ing   bra___e   instru___ted   ro___et

sla___   magneti___   ___linch   fla___e   Atlanti___

Write the word with the suffix on the line. Follow spelling rules as needed.   **(10 points)**

thin + est   = _thinnest_

fix + es   = _____   crave + ing   = _____

swipe+ ed   = _____   publish + er   = _____

hid + en   = _____   splendid + ly = _____

complete + ing= _____   spin + er   = _____

flip + ed   = _____   retire + ment = _____

Match prefixes and roots to their meaning. Indicate if it is a prefix or root.   **(20 points)**

Indicate Prefix or Root	Prefix/Root	Meaning
Ex: __prefix__	en	throw
1. _____	1. pend	out of, away from
2. _____	2. ject	trust
3. _____	3. ex	hang
4. _____	4. dis	in, into, within
5. _____	5. fid	wrongly, bad
6. _____	6. mis	not, opposite of
7. _____	7. trans	to build
8. _____	8. lect	across, beyond
9. _____	9. sens	choose
10. _____	10. struct	feeling

WILSON® Just Words®

Name _____

1. _____

2. _____

3. _____

4. _____

5. _____

6. _____

7. _____

8. _____

9. _____

10. _____

11. _____

12. _____

13. _____

14. _____

15. _____

1. a (different) crusade

2. (mother) is tidy

3. (laugh) rudely

4. storm in the (country)

5. (until) we memorize

6. is (usually) discarded

7. (although) it is repealed

8. uncoil (new) rope

9. crouch for a (minute)

10. (people) will flaunt

11. (every) dimple

12. a (beautiful) quotation

13. inclusion with (others)

14. dependable (enough)

15. quibbled (again)

(HF Words)   = _____ / 15
+ Phonetic Words = _____ / 15
   Total   = _____ / 30

Divide each word below into syllables. Read the word. Write the syllables on the lines and mark syllables.

program = <u>prō</u>   <u>grăm</u>
          o   c

edit = <u>ĕd</u>   <u>ĭt</u>
     c   c

pretend = _____ _____

donate = _____ _____

stupid = _____ _____

polite = _____ _____

deduct = _____ _____

credit = _____ _____

frozen = _____ _____

refund = _____ _____

rodent = _____ _____

model = _____ _____

reject = _____ _____

comic = _____ _____

provide = _____ _____

dilate = _____ _____

require = _____ _____

profit = _____ _____

vomit = _____ _____

hotel = _____ _____

radish = _____ _____

document = _____ _____ _____

comprehend = _____ _____ _____

regulate = _____ _____ _____

Divide each word below into syllables. Write the syllables on the lines. Mark syllables and y sound.

cozy   =   cō   zȳ /ē/   crazy   = _____ _____

nasty   = _____ _____   lobby   = _____ _____

tidy   = _____ _____   ruby   = _____ _____

rally   = _____ _____   envy   = _____ _____

Write the word with the suffix on the line. Underline baseword and circle suffix. Mark spelling rules as appropriate.

1-1-1 + ly, ty, y

glad + ly = glad(ly)

snob + y = snobb(y)

grim + ly = _____

six + ty = _____

thin + ly = _____

sun + y = _____

crab + y = _____

sad + ly = _____

bag + y = _____

fog + y = _____

v-e + ly, ty, y

haze + y = haz(y) ᵉ

nine + y = nine(ty)

remote + ly = _____

entire + ly = _____

time + ly = _____

bone + y = _____

complete + ly = _____

safe + ty = _____

safe + ly = _____

slime + y = _____

PHRASE PRACTICE

now can **fly**

now does **require**

knew **he** was **spry**

donate new things

knew to **be silent**

should **be humid**

locate new home

beware of dog

will know in a **moment**

know the **defect**

must now **migrate**

should now **hydrate**

request to use

know how to **decode**

now know **myself**

comprehend the **document**

depend on a friend

desire to know

has a new **banjo**

friend in a **crisis**

MARK UP BOLD WORDS

"Scoop" and mark syllables.

WILSON® Just Words® | ©2009 Wilson Language Training Corporation

PHRASE PRACTICE

class **entirely empty**

pantry is full

penny was new

not only **funny**

pick any **puppy**

their only **duty**

silly old game

many pretty **tulips**

many are **angry**

envy many friends

---

must **strongly** defend

will **gladly** predict

was at the **rally**

lady with **floppy** hat

fell **flatly** on **belly**

will **bravely decline**

spoke **bluntly**

only **nutty** muffin

began when **foggy**

golf with a **caddy**

MARK UP BOLD WORDS

"Scoop" the baseword into syllables, and circle any suffixes.
Mark syllables in baseword. Indicate the sound of **y** as /ē/.

A Well-Behaved Puppy

A dog can be a human's best friend. They come in all shapes and sizes, but all pets are dependent upon humans. If you want your puppy to thrive, you must help it to become a well-behaved dog. You must connect with your puppy and expect him to behave. Dogs desire to make you happy so the lessons that you give it when it is just a pup will prevent problems and stop bad habits for its lifetime.

It is no secret: when a puppy misbehaves, just say no! It is up to you to prevent any destructive acts. It takes time to get it to recall your commands and you must provide that time. It also takes some skill. It is vital to get your puppy to behave with only nonviolent methods. If it misbehaves, reprimand it, but do not hit it. You must develop a close bond with your puppy. It must know that it belongs. It has to know where it fits into the pecking order in your family. You should also take the time to expose your dog to other canines and to other people. This will help it be confident.

Sometimes your puppy will reject a command that you give. It could grab an item and refuse to give it back to you. It is not acting like that to spite you! Dogs, resembling people, like to know what is expected of them. The basic "golden" rule is to be consistent. That is - expect the puppy to do your command every time! If your puppy is biting you, it is best to stop it quickly. You do not want to have snappy fangs nipping into you. You can simply pull your hand back and yelp to let it know that you did not like it.

Your small puppy depends upon you and it is your duty to take care of it. Be sure to have plenty of fun with it too! You will not regret it at all. With your help and care, your puppy will become a great dog. In the end, your small, cuddly canine can truly become a fantastic pet for its lifetime and the best friend you could ever have!

PHRASES FOR CHARTING

only provide some

any small documents

knew their duty

now frozen solid

begin the new rally

my golf caddy

prepare to vacate

many safety glasses

now windy and chilly

sunny and cozy

should hydrate now

comprehend and know

the pretty pantry

many are empty

a filthy hotel

barely a protest

Student Name: _____   *Unit#* _____   *Test Date:* _____

SOUNDS

1 _____   2 _____   3 _____

WORDS

1 _____   6 _____

2 _____   7 _____

3 _____   8 _____

4 _____   9 _____

5 _____   10 _____

PHRASES

1 _____   3 _____

2 _____   4 _____

SENTENCES

1 _____

_____

2 _____

_____

UNIT SCORES

SOUNDS	_____ /3	MARKING	_____ /2 (☐ All elements of task 1 ☐ All elements of task 2)
PHONETIC WORDS	_____ /20	CAPITALIZATION	_____ /2 (☐ Sentence 1 ☐ Sentence 2)
HIGH FREQUENCY WORDS	_____ /10	PUNCTUATION	_____ /2 (☐ Sentence 1 ☐ Sentence 2)
		LEGIBILITY	_____ /1 (☐ All writing is legible)

THIS PAGE IS INTENTIONALLY LEFT BLANK

Name _____

1. _____

2. _____

3. _____

4. _____

5. _____

6. _____

7. _____

8. _____

9. _____

10. _____

11. _____

12. _____

13. _____

14. _____

15. _____

1. (many) can <u>relate</u>

2. (always) <u>crazy</u>

3. the <u>costly</u> (work)

4. (near) the <u>marsh</u>

5. (mountain) and <u>forest</u>

6. the (other) <u>compartment</u>

7. <u>feast</u> to (please)

8. (people) will <u>deploy</u>

9. (father) is <u>youthful</u>

10. (although) it was <u>haunted</u>

11. (always) <u>rambles</u>

12. (our) <u>calculation</u>

13. the (only) <u>revision</u>

14. (trouble) when <u>demolished</u>

15. (caught) the <u>bundles</u>

(HF Words)   = _____ / 15
+ <u>Phonetic Words</u> = _____ / 15
  Total   = _____ / 30

Progress Check Unit 9

Read the words. Mark the syllables closed, open, v-e and r-controlled.

swerve r	burnt	share
brake	blame	churn
harsh	spent	spine
bask	pro	chomp
spy	quirk	curve

Write the option letters on the blanks provided. Use a dictionary or electronic spell checker to determine the correct spelling. Write the correct spelling on the line provided.

er, **ir**, or **ur**?

c _er_ ve ____curve____	n____ve _____	bl____t _____
c _ir_ ve	n____ve	bl____t
c _ur_ ve	n____ve	bl____t
wh____l _____	squ____t _____	ch____n _____
wh____l	squ____t	ch____n
wh____l	squ____t	ch____n
sw____l _____	b____st _____	f____m _____
sw____l	b____st	f____m
sw____l	b____st	f____m
st____n _____	th____st _____	j____k _____
st____n	th____st	j____k
st____n	th____st	j____k
sw____ve _____	b____nt _____	c____b _____
sw____ve	b____nt	c____b
sw____ve	b____nt	c____b
b____th _____	bl____ _____	p____ch _____
b____th	bl____	p____ch
b____th	bl____	p____ch

Write the word with the suffix on the line. Follow spelling rules as needed.

marsh + es = ___marshes___   swerve + ed = ___swerved___

scorch + es = _____   harm + ful = _____

slur + ing = _____   stir + ed = _____

flirt + ed = _____   squirt + ing = _____

serve + ing = _____   torch + ed = _____

tar + ing = _____   starve + ing = _____

fur + y = _____   jar + ed = _____

fur + less = _____   blur + y = _____

bark + ing = _____   smirk + ed = _____

star + y = _____   burn + er = _____

spur + ed = _____   quirk + y = _____

PHRASE PRACTICE

ar, or = /ər/

sort every year

very large **arch**

move large **fort**

every new **dorm**

start every car

should get a **spark**

the new **harp**

friend in the **yard**

sport of the year

very **harsh** punishment

ee, ir, ur = /ər/

large **bird perch**

in the **first term**

lost **her nerve**

many at **church**

twirl the large stick

surf on the web

her first girl

is quite **stern**

serve the lunch

very long **turn**

MARK UP BOLD WORDS

Mark the r-controlled syllables.

PHRASE PRACTICE

four pretty **girls**

these four **storms**

only our **cards**

perches very close

they learn **darts**

serving us lunch

barks any hour

scarred from the fall

our only **stars**

hidden in **marshes**

only four **porches**

use many **charts**

charred by fire

swerved into place

perched on the throne

starring the best

four small **chirps**

learn it was **hurtful**

stirred our pot

all was **blurry**

MARK UP BOLD WORDS

"Scoop" the baseword into syllables. Mark the word.

When Storms are Destructive

Storms are not the same everywhere on Earth. In fact, there are many kinds of storms.

If you live in a place that is dry and windy you know about sandstorms. These storms are common over dry land and they can lift and deposit dust miles away. Dust from a swirling windstorm can sting and can be very harsh.

Gale winds are thirty-nine to fifty-five miles per hour, but hurricane winds are at a constant speed of seventy-four miles per hour or more. A hurricane brings a large burst of rain and strong wind gusts for many hours. These strong winds can even lift and hurl large objects including cars and homes. These storms must be carefully tracked as they cross the Atlantic or the Gulf of Mexico.

If you were born in the north, you know about a different kind of storm. A snowstorm that starts in the dark of the night can blanket everything. When you wake up, the land before you is suddenly all white. It is pretty for sure, but you quickly learn that it is not much fun to be out during that storm.

Some people have hard jobs that require a constant storm watch. They quickly learn to make it part of their duty everyday. Fishermen must be smart and carefully chart their travel every hour so that the surf of a storm does not take their fishing vessel, especially if it is a small craft.

Most storms do not bring about much harm, but some can be quite destructive. You must be smart. When at home or afar, be sure you are safe when the next storm comes your way. Get the forecast and then get inside. Unless duty calls, be sure that you do not make the mistake of going out in a bad storm.

PHRASES FOR CHARTING

1   DETERMINE SCORE

→ TOTAL WORDS READ	
− ERRORS	
= WORDS READ CORRECTLY	

2   CHART PROGRESS

GRAPH YOUR SCORE ON THE "MY PROGRESS" CHART FOR THIS UNIT

twirl for an hour

very harsh year

girl was born

our four cards

starring the wildest

learn to march

more will burst

burnt the pork

into the large jar

compare the charts

swerved to miss

with every turn

friend has nerve

very wet marsh

serving us brunch

sort into piles

Student Name: _____ *Unit#* _____ *Test Date:* _____

SOUNDS

1 _____ 2 _____ 3 _____

WORDS

1 _____ 6 _____

2 _____ 7 _____

3 _____ 8 _____

4 _____ 9 _____

5 _____ 10 _____

PHRASES

1 _____ 3 _____

2 _____ 4 _____

SENTENCES

1 _____

_____

2 _____

_____

UNIT SCORES

SOUNDS _____ /3   MARKING _____ /2 (❑ All elements of task 1 ❑ All elements of task 2)

PHONETIC WORDS _____ /20   CAPITALIZATION _____ /2 (❑ Sentence 1 ❑ Sentence 2)

HIGH FREQUENCY WORDS _____ /10   PUNCTUATION _____ /2 (❑ Sentence 1 ❑ Sentence 2)

LEGIBILITY _____ /1 (❑ All writing is legible)

THIS PAGE IS INTENTIONALLY LEFT BLANK

Name _____

1. _____

2. _____

3. _____

4. _____

5. _____

6. _____

7. _____

8. _____

9. _____

10. _____

11. _____

12. _____

13. _____

14. _____

15. _____

(HF Words) = _____ / 15
+ <u>Phonetic Words</u> = _____ / 15
Total = _____ / 30

1. (many) have <u>spoken</u>

2. (buy) that <u>ruby</u>

3. (four) <u>crispy</u> wings

4. (about) to <u>starve</u>

5. (year) for <u>ordering</u>

6. (always) <u>tormented</u>

7. was <u>indeed</u> (pretty)

8. <u>ointment</u> had (color)

9. (because) he <u>frowned</u>

10. last (minute) <u>overhaul</u>

11. did <u>fumble</u> (again)

12. a (large) <u>distraction</u>

13. (trouble) with <u>provisions</u>

14. <u>expandable</u> (ocean)

15. (usually) <u>struggled</u>

Progress Check Unit 10

Divide the words and write the syllables on the lines. Mark the syllable types and read the words.

memorize = <u>měm</u> (or) <u>īzͤ</u>   absorbent = _____ _____ _____
         c   r   v-e

argument = _____ _____ _____   forest = _____ _____

horizon = _____ _____ _____   bombardment = _____ _____ _____

organize = _____ _____ _____   porcupine = _____ _____ _____

formulate = _____ _____ _____   sarcastic = _____ _____ _____

harmony = _____ _____ _____   organic = _____ _____ _____

embargo = _____ _____ _____   misinform = _____ _____ _____

arthritis = _____ _____ _____   department = _____ _____ _____

platform = _____ _____   harmonize = _____ _____ _____

shortstop = _____ _____   distort = _____ _____

passport = _____ _____   party = _____ _____

harvest = _____ _____   remark = _____ _____

Divide the words and write the syllables on the lines. Mark the syllable types and read the words.

interstate = <u>ĭn</u> <u>tĕr</u> <u>stāte</u>
              c   r   v-e

cucumber = _____ _____ _____

partnership = _____ _____ _____

advertise = _____ _____ _____

murmur = _____ _____

flattery = _____ _____ _____

archery = _____ _____ _____

turpentine = _____ _____ _____

imperfect = _____ _____ _____

perjury = _____ _____ _____

Consider the three options for each word. Choose one to write on the line provided. Use a dictionary or electronic spell checker to verify the correct spelling.

er, **ir**, or **ur**?

plast<u>er</u> <u>plaster</u>	conf____m _____	p____mit _____
plast<u>ir</u>	conf____m	p____mit
plast<u>ur</u>	conf____m	p____mit
s____vive _____	st____dy _____	timb____ _____
s____vive	st____dy	timb____
s____vive	st____dy	timb____
int____com _____	p____sist _____	th____mostat _____
int____com	p____sist	th____mostat
int____com	p____sist	th____mostat
consid____ _____	obs____ve _____	t____bulent _____
consid____	obs____ve	t____bulent
consid____	obs____ve	t____bulent
flatt____y _____	int____vene _____	int____nship _____
flatt____y	int____vene	int____nship
flatt____y	int____vene	int____nship

PHRASE PRACTICE

had another **partnership**   to **garnish** the dish

in our new **garden**   **bombard** the earth

use some **garlic**   the other large **shipyard**

answer their **horoscope**   another pretty **garment**

orbit our Earth   the large **market**

---

carbon from Earth   to **forbid** the child

forty years old   **torment** their friends

some other **department**   **formulate** the answer

use another **florist**   **history** of the Earth

from another **tornado**   in the other **compartment**

MARK UP BOLD WORDS

"Scoop" and mark syllables.

PHRASE PRACTICE

percolate the water

tolerate the work

learn the **adverb**

was very **persistent**

survive turbulent water

very **murky** water

father should **consider**

put your **dirty** shirts

mother would **suffer**

above the **banner**

furnish the apartment

observing father work

confirm the **lobster permit**

verdict was harsh

to **conserve** the cash

mother has **bursitis**

further from home

work in a **nursery**

stop the **skirmish**

smart as an **expert**

MARK UP BOLD WORDS

"Scoop" and mark syllables.

Exploring the North Pole

Would you like to be an explorer - not just any explorer, but the first one to get to the North Pole? I wonder if you would like to be the person who once said, "I think I am the first man to sit on top of the world!"

Matt Henson was with Commander Admiral Peary on a cold morning in 1909 when they firmly planted an American flag at the North Pole. The exploring party consisted of Henson, Robert Peary and four Inuit people. Over the years, there has been controversy as to who was the first person, Peary or Henson, to arrive there. Admiral Peary led the party, but it was Henson, an African American, who had learned so many important skills to help get them there.

Matt Henson was born on a farm in Maryland. When his father and mother both died, he worked as a cabin boy on a merchant ship. He was twelve or thirteen years old at the time. The ship's skipper taught Henson how to read and write. Matt also mastered the skills of a navigator and mapmaker. Later, Henson met Robert Peary, and Peary asked him to be an assistant on trips with him. For years, they made trips together and then became arctic explorers. It was also at this time that Henson learned many things from the Inuit people, who were skilled arctic travelers. He learned fishing, hunting and sled making.

Commander Peary and Henson made several attempts to get to the North Pole before they finally made it there. In 1906, they made a trip that came up short when a river of open water separated them from the North Pole. In 1909, they formulated a plan for another attempt. They set out with 246 dogs to pull sleds full of people, food and equipment, which was hardly modern. By the time they got to the North Pole, there were only six left in the party. We cannot be sure what exactly happened next, but we do know for sure that Henson and Peary sat together at the top of the Earth on that arctic morning in 1909.

If you are ever in Aspen Hill, Maryland, you can visit the Matthew Henson State Park. In New York, you can also visit the landmark where Henson later lived, the Dunbar Apartments in Harlem. If you visit history in person or just ponder Henson exploring the North Pole, be sure to stop a moment and think about yourself sitting on top of the world!

PHRASES FOR CHARTING

organize your answer

formulate a plan

any other department

consider this water

place another lantern

the charming merchant

work with a florist

best partnership on Earth

confirm the birthrate

another pretty morning

observed his mother

compare the glory

further from conflict

another sarcastic story

father cleverly banned

learned the adverb

1 DETERMINE SCORE

→ TOTAL WORDS READ	
− ERRORS	
= WORDS READ CORRECTLY	

2 CHART PROGRESS

GRAPH YOUR SCORE ON THE "MY PROGRESS" CHART FOR THIS UNIT

Student Name: _____ *Unit#* _____ *Test Date:* _____

SOUNDS

1 _____ 2 _____ 3 _____

WORDS

1 _____ 6 _____

2 _____ 7 _____

3 _____ 8 _____

4 _____ 9 _____

5 _____ 10 _____

PHRASES

1 _____ 3 _____

2 _____ 4 _____

SENTENCES

1 _____

_____

2 _____

_____

UNIT SCORES

SOUNDS _____ /3   MARKING _____ /2 (☐ All elements of task 1 ☐ All elements of task 2)

PHONETIC WORDS _____ /20   CAPITALIZATION _____ /2 (☐ Sentence 1 ☐ Sentence 2)

HIGH FREQUENCY WORDS _____ /10   PUNCTUATION _____ /2 (☐ Sentence 1 ☐ Sentence 2)

LEGIBILITY _____ /1 (☐ All writing is legible)

THIS PAGE IS INTENTIONALLY LEFT BLANK

WILSON® Just Words®

Name _____

1. _____
2. _____
3. _____
4. _____
5. _____
6. _____
7. _____
8. _____
9. _____
10. _____
11. _____
12. _____
13. _____
14. _____
15. _____

1. (only) <u>protected</u> one
2. (very) <u>cozy</u>
3. (always) <u>classy</u>
4. (father) did <u>carve</u>
5. (change) <u>partners</u>
6. (laugh) in <u>harmony</u>
7. a (high) <u>screech</u>
8. (caught) in the <u>convoy</u>
9. (people) are <u>drowning</u>
10. <u>unlawful</u> (trouble)
11. to <u>staple</u> (around)
12. (another) <u>conviction</u>
13. last (minute) <u>exclusion</u>
14. (different) <u>requirement</u>
15. (although) he <u>gobbled</u>

(HF Words) = _____ / 15
+ <u>Phonetic Words</u> = _____ / 15
Total = _____ / 30

Progress Check Unit 11

Add **ai** or **ay** to each word. Use a dictionary or electronic spell checker as needed. Rewrite the whole word.

qu_ai_nt = ___quaint___	displ___ = _____
rem___nder = _____	obt___ned = _____
portr___ing = _____	del___s = _____
rep___red = _____	r___ndrop = _____
cont___ner = _____	ess___ = _____
betr___ = _____	w___stline = _____

Add **ee**, **ea**, or **ey** to each word. Use a dictionary or electronic spell checker as needed. Rewrite the whole word.

voll_ey_ = ___volley___	fr___dom = _____
bl___k = _____	st___mer = _____
hock___ = _____	parsl___ = _____
fl___t = _____	coff___ = _____
est___m = _____	jers___s = _____
b___ting = _____	ind___d = _____

Divide the words and write the syllables on the lines. Mark the syllable types and read the words.

rejoin = <u>rĕ</u> <u>join</u>
        o   d

deploy = ____ ____

turmoil = ____ ____

convoy = ____ ____

sirloin = ____ ____

ointment = ____ ____

tinfoil = ____ ____

uncoil = ____ ____

enjoy = ____ ____

overjoy = ____ ____ ____

employ = ____ ____

asteroid = ____ ____ ____

Combine the basewords and suffixes into words and write them on the lines.

pray + ing = <u>praying</u>

plenty + ful = <u>plentiful</u>

stay + ed = _____

volley + ing = _____

jersey + s = _____

fry + ed = _____

gray + ing = _____

overjoy + ed = _____

play + er = _____

galaxy + es = _____

happy + est = _____

tally + ed = _____

nifty + est = _____

lucky + est = _____

enjoy + ing = _____

valley + s = _____

sloppy + ness = _____

bossy + est = _____

dressy + er = _____

cry + er = _____

donkey + s = _____

play + ful = _____

employ + ment = _____

tangy + ness = _____

PHRASE PRACTICE

ai, ay = /ā/

more to **obtain**

a pretty **bridesmaid**

when you **strain**

may I please

have great **faith**

four water **containers**

remain right here

decay in the earth

pray for **rainfall**

please **pay** the **bail**

ee, ey, ea = /ē/

beehive was high

use the **screen**

please the **jockey**

great **hockey** game **indeed**

need to turn right

between great **leaders**

levee was high

the right **sneakers**

had **thirteen treats**

very high **cheekbones**

MARK UP BOLD WORDS

"Scoop" syllables and circle any suffix. Mark syllables in baseword.

PHRASE PRACTICE

oi, oy = /oi/

could **spoil** the child

through all the **turmoil**

although **tinfoil** is best

boycott is enough

a kink in the **joint**

thought it was **noisy**

dig through the **topsoil**

the **paperboy** thought

enough solid **employment**

will **enjoy** it enough

y spelling rule

done with the **flies**

to locate other **galaxies**

thought they were **spies**

volleying to win

the **silliest** game

dried up completely

stayed quite discreet

the **messiest** mistake

made enough **copies**

many are **graying**

MARK UP BOLD WORDS

Top list: "Scoop" and mark syllables.

Bottom list: Underline baseword and circle suffix,
indicating spelling rules as needed.

Painting On Your Mind

Have you ever dreamed that you could be a master artist someday? Perhaps you will be one of the greatest painters who ever lived, but if not, you could still be considered a wonderful artist indeed. What truly matters most is that you enjoy your projects. If you have studied art, you know that there is no right way to paint. Although you are free to go with your thoughts and do what you wish, art classes will teach you some of the things that great painters have done.

Some people prefer to paint landscapes such as river banks or rainfall in a valley. Other people like to do abstract shapes and modern or contemporary work. Some artists portray joyful subjects that please them, whereas others prefer to express sadness with their paintbrush. Each form is interesting to study. The paintings of Norman Rockwell, for example, portray American life the way it was many years ago. His work will surely entertain you with the high detail of his subjects.

Some people prefer to do painting that is used for embellishing objects called decorative painting. This is done on glass, fabrics such as silk, other textiles and even home furnishings such as lamps. It can even be done on a wall! Can you see in your mind how an artist could display star galaxies on a high wall?

If you have the opportunity to visit several art galleries, it will inspire you! It is amazing to see some great artwork displayed. When you go, you could study the different kinds of work. It is fun to point out some of the aspects used by each artist, but do not try to explain all of the paintings. Just enjoy! Perhaps if you are lucky enough, you could see a great oil painting that has survived through the years or the amazing work of a master artist.

So pick up a paintbrush and have fun. Simply entertain yourself and the people around you. Or who knows, perhaps you could obtain employment as a painter or even be the next Rembrandt!

PHRASES FOR CHARTING

1 DETERMINE SCORE

→ TOTAL WORDS READ
− ERRORS
= WORDS READ CORRECTLY

2 CHART PROGRESS

GRAPH YOUR SCORE ON THE "MY PROGRESS" CHART FOR THIS UNIT

rejoined the army

needed the rainfall

the greatest painting

trail through deep valleys

saving your pennies

the right subway

okay to destroy

thought it was sillier

obtain high marks

the noisiest train

explain the galaxies

not enough weekdays

new hockey jerseys

please green beast

enough painful thoughts

although she pointed

Student Name: _____ *Unit#* _____ *Test Date:* _____

SOUNDS

1 _____ 2 _____ 3 _____

WORDS

1 _____ 6 _____

2 _____ 7 _____

3 _____ 8 _____

4 _____ 9 _____

5 _____ 10 _____

PHRASES

1 _____ 3 _____

2 _____ 4 _____

SENTENCES

1 _____

_____

2 _____

_____

UNIT SCORES

SOUNDS _____ /3   MARKING _____ /2 (❑ All elements of task 1 ❑ All elements of task 2)

PHONETIC WORDS _____ /20   CAPITALIZATION _____ /2 (❑ Sentence 1 ❑ Sentence 2)

HIGH FREQUENCY WORDS _____ /10   PUNCTUATION _____ /2 (❑ Sentence 1 ❑ Sentence 2)

LEGIBILITY _____ /1 (❑ All writing is legible)

THIS PAGE IS INTENTIONALLY LEFT BLANK

Name _____

1. _____

2. _____

3. _____

4. _____

5. _____

6. _____

7. _____

8. _____

9. _____

10. _____

11. _____

12. _____

13. _____

14. _____

15. _____

(HF Words)   = _____ / 15
+ Phonetic Words   = _____ / 15
   Total   = _____ / 30

1. <u>depend</u> on (another)

2. <u>envy</u> the (beautiful) one

3. (work) in <u>safety</u>

4. <u>scorches</u> the (earth)

5. (about) to <u>harvest</u>

6. <u>chartering</u> by the (hour)

7. (near) his <u>kidney</u>

8. (follow) the <u>tabloid</u>

9. is (usually) <u>rowdy</u>

10. (because) it is <u>authentic</u>

11. <u>muffle</u> the (laugh)

12. (until) the <u>adoption</u>

13. (mountain) <u>erosion</u>

14. it was <u>blemished</u> (again)

15. (always) <u>humbling</u>

Determine correct spelling for the sound of /ō/ (**o-e, o, oa, ow, oe**). Write word and mark syllables.

thr __oa__ t   = ___throat___
ᵈ

m ___ er   = _____

c ___ stline   = _____

tipt ___   = _____

shall ___   = _____

cr ___   = _____

fl ___ ting   = _____

gr ___ th   = _____

cockr ___ ch   = _____

sh ___ ing   = _____

charc ___ l   = _____

fl ___ n   = _____

Determine correct spelling for the sound of /ou/ (**ou, ow**). Write word and mark syllables.

p __ow__ er   = ___power___
ᵈ   ʳ

___ tside   = _____

disc ___ nt   = _____

r ___ dy   = _____

boysc ___ t   = _____

b ___ nd   = _____

b ___ nty   = _____

ch ___ der   = _____

c ___ nty   = _____

___ tstanding   = _____

t ___ el   = _____

s ___ nded   = _____

Determine correct spelling for the sound of /ü/ (**u**, **u-e**, **ou**, **oo**, **ue**). Write word and mark syllables.

t _u_ ne = _tŭne_   y____th = _____
v-e

gr____p = _____   f____lish = _____

st____l = _____   tatt____ = _____

st____dent = _____   s____p = _____

aven____ = _____   intr____de = _____

Determine sound of **oo**: /ü/ as in school or /u̇/ as in book.

shook - oo = _/u̇/_   spooky - oo = ____   spoon - oo = ____

stool - oo = _/ü/_   childhood - oo = ____   hooked - oo = ____

Determine correct spelling for the sound of /ȯ/ (**aw**, **au**). Write word and mark syllables.

withdr _aw_ = _withdraw_   fl____less = _____
c   d

s____dust = _____   ____gust = _____

fr____d = _____   r____ = _____

____thentic = _____   f____lt = _____

exh____st = _____   cr____ling = _____

l____ndry = _____   astron____t = _____

PHRASE PRACTICE

oa, oe, ow = /ō/

full of **foam**	will follow the **coach**
croak of a **toad**	**rainbow** of color
about two **shiploads**	**shown** at the mall
color of his **toe**	**crowbar** to move it
very large **elbow**	was about to **tiptoe**

ow, ou = /ou/

to follow the **crowd**	right to **empower**
a great **scoutmaster**	too many to **roundup**
bound with rope	a different **tower**
shout from the top	**crouch** behind **couch**
an **unfounded** report	a different **clown**

MARK UP BOLD WORDS

"Scoop" and mark syllables.

PHRASE PRACTICE

ue, ew, ou, oo = /ü/

foolish to laugh

because of a **loophole**

rooster did crow

drew another **cartoon**

mountain in **bloom**

rescue from the mountain

ballroom for **soup**

caught the **group**

his **cue** to laugh

taxes were **due**

au, aw = /ȯ/

made the **author** laugh

draw an **astronaut**

laundry was filthy

an **authentic** rainbow

caught in the **vault**

overhaul every car

mountain was **haunted**

withdraw my vote

autopsy gave **proof**

yawn then laugh

MARK UP BOLD WORDS

"Scoop" and mark syllables.

Alternative Power Now!

All over our Earth, a large amount of power is used every day. Because of this, people need to work for the development of alternative energy and support different approaches to power. This is important for powering our cars and homes so that we do not just depend upon oil and other fossil fuels.

Hybrid cars are an alternative to solely gas-powered cars. There are electric and hydraulic hybrids. Motorists should consider these for their travel. It is foolish to ignore the need for better fuel economy. Hybrids can help to lessen the amount of gas and oil that is used everyday. The electric hybrids are powered by storing electricity in the battery when a car slows down. Other hybrids use hydraulic power, storing energy in the form of compressed gas. The hydraulic hybrids could be more useful for buses and delivery vans that make frequent stops. The batteries for hybrids are bulky, but should be downsized over time.

Alternative energy must also be found to power our homes and places of work. One such alternative, the use of wind turbines, is growing rapidly. When many turbines work together, it is called a wind farm. Wind farms can be constructed off the coastline, as well as on land. The blades of a wind turbine are so big, they are difficult to transport on roads. However, ships can transport large components over water to the site of a wind farm that is located in the ocean.

Wind provides clean energy, but some people oppose these wind farms. When wind farms in the ocean were first proposed, opponents said these farms would interfere with radar signals, fishermen, other boats and airplanes. They also felt that the farms could spoil a pretty view. Supporters said that the turbines in the water off the coastline provided electric power that was needed on the surrounding land. They begged people to please consider the overall outcome.

People everywhere need to work and find ways to continue the development and use of these and other energy alternatives. It is important to follow through and subdue the environmental impact on Earth!

PHRASES FOR CHARTING

1 DETERMINE SCORE

a grand ballroom

follow the last clue

→ TOTAL WORDS READ	
− ERRORS	
= WORDS READ CORRECTLY	

laugh about laundry

empower the crowd

2 CHART PROGRESS

GRAPH YOUR SCORE ON THE "MY PROGRESS" CHART FOR THIS UNIT

want crawfish soup

shout from mountain

group should bemoan

a different shampoo

color of the rainbow

gloated about victory

caught with hook

the aloe ointment

four foolish cartoons

withdrew because of fraud

airplane is grounded

taxes overdue

Student Name: _____ *Unit#* _____ *Test Date:* _____

SOUNDS

1 _____ 2 _____ 3 _____

WORDS

1 _____ 6 _____

2 _____ 7 _____

3 _____ 8 _____

4 _____ 9 _____

5 _____ 10 _____

PHRASES

1 _____ 3 _____

2 _____ 4 _____

SENTENCES

1 _____

_____

2 _____

_____

UNIT SCORES

SOUNDS _____ /3   MARKING _____ /2 (☐ All elements of task 1 ☐ All elements of task 2)

PHONETIC WORDS _____ /20   CAPITALIZATION _____ /2 (☐ Sentence 1 ☐ Sentence 2)

HIGH FREQUENCY WORDS _____ /10   PUNCTUATION _____ /2 (☐ Sentence 1 ☐ Sentence 2)

LEGIBILITY _____ /1 (☐ All writing is legible)

THIS PAGE IS INTENTIONALLY LEFT BLANK

Name _____

1. _____

2. _____

3. _____

4. _____

5. _____

6. _____

7. _____

8. _____

9. _____

10. _____

11. _____

12. _____

13. _____

14. _____

15. _____

1. (learn) for the <u>debate</u>

2. (always) <u>nasty</u>

3. <u>consistently</u> (work)

4. <u>sparks</u> (trouble)

5. (knew) of the <u>argument</u>

6. <u>transported</u> to the (country)

7. <u>cheapest</u> (water)

8. (people) will <u>loiter</u>

9. (although) it is <u>outstanding</u>

10. (thought) to be <u>flawless</u>

11. (buy) a <u>bundle</u>

12. a <u>location</u> (away)

13. (another) <u>explosion</u>

14. (through) the <u>investment</u>

15. (because) it is <u>drizzling</u>

Progress Check Unit 13

(HF Words) = _____ / 15
+ <u>Phonetic Words</u> = _____ / 15
Total = _____ / 30

Read the words. Write the syllables on the lines. Mark the syllables and vowels.

muffle = __mŭf__ __fle__
             c   -le

bugle = _____ _____

battle = _____ _____

sample = _____ _____

title = _____ _____

puzzle = _____ _____

maple = _____ _____

thimble = _____ _____

struggle = _____ _____

ramble = _____ _____

noble = _____ _____

brittle = _____ _____

scuffle = _____ _____

staple = _____ _____

mumble = _____ _____

gamble = _____ _____

baffle = _____ _____

fable = _____ _____

gable = _____ _____

cradle = _____ _____

Add the suffix to the words below.

rattle + ing = __răttling__
                  c -le

puzzle + ment = _____

freckle + s = _____

staple + ing = _____

tattle + er = _____

pebble + s = _____

wiggle + ing = _____

fable + s = _____

huddle + ed = _____

settle + ment = _____

Read the words. Write the syllables on the lines. Box the **sion**, **ssion**, **tion** welded sounds.

lotion = lo ⟦tion⟧

option = ___ ___

mission = ___ ___

inclusion = ___ ___ ___

invasion = ___ ___ ___

explosion = ___ ___ ___

expansion = ___ ___ ___

consumption = ___ ___ ___

relaxation = ___ ___ ___ ___

compassion = ___ ___ ___

comprehension = ___ ___ ___ ___

completion = ___ ___ ___

Read the words below. List the words above in the correct columns below.

---

suspension   protection   extension   dictation

discussion   transfusion   concussion   infection

confusion   conclusion   explosion   emotion

tion = /shŭn/   **sion = /shŭn/**   **sion = /zhŭn/**

_____   _____   _____

_____   _____   _____

_____   _____   _____

_____   _____   _____

PHRASE PRACTICE

people could **battle**	the beautiful **table**
puddle is trouble	people **struggle** enough
always will **sizzle**	place above **candle**
always will **tumble**	**staple** three sheets
buckles with trouble	did always **giggle**

stumbles into people	was always **unstable**
shall always **tremble**	more water **bottles**
the beautiful **jungle**	always **juggle** more
through the **puddle**	**beagle** was trouble
and other **staples**	**resembles** beautiful people

MARK UP BOLD WORDS

"Scoop" and mark syllables.

PHRASE PRACTICE

buy more **lotion**

every **combination**

sent away for **invention**

pick another **option**

introduction of our country

buy our **admission**

education about ocean

away from **explosion**

through more **instruction**

not their **vision**

buy your **pension**

mention the trainer

prevention of illness

elbow has an **infection**

because of the **concussion**

objection to the rule

a **dimension** away

country for **relaxation**

thought about **mission**

description of ocean

MARK UP BOLD WORDS

"Scoop" and mark syllables.

Great Inventions Don't Just Happen

Did you ever want to make a great invention? Start your exploration of a topic by doing lots of reading and studying today! The story of the first powered airplane is an example of how reading can lead to great things.

In a historic moment in 1903, Orville and Wilbur Wright finally flew a powered aircraft along the ocean on a remote beach location in Kitty Hawk, North Carolina. It was something they had dreamed about for a long time. On their first attempt there was trouble. The biplane toppled to the left and mangled the wing. When they tried a few days later, both Orville and Wilbur flew the biplane! They quickly contacted their father with instructions to inform the press about their excursion. Their invention astounded people.

Reading and step-by-step investigation played a key role in the innovation of the biplane. When the two men were boys, they lived in a home that had two beautiful libraries with a very large collection of books! When Wilbur was nineteen, he endured heart palpitations and stayed home to care for his mother for the next four years. During this time, his obsession with reading helped give him quite a foundation of facts.

Later, Wilbur and his brother Orville owned a bike shop.

Despite this diversion, they set out to learn all that they could about the subject of flying. They gathered information and facts with the desire to unlock the secrets needed to master flying. Although they puzzled over things, they did not let these questions baffle them. The construction of an aircraft that would function properly became their single mission.

You can be sure the operation of the plane that day did not just happen. Wilbur and Orville had the intention of flying, and they had to tackle this by cutting the big problem down into smaller solutions. It took so much collaboration. They first mastered the art of gliding before they developed the powered aircraft. After much research, they developed a three-axis control which helped to enable one to steer the plane. This is still used on fixed-wing aircraft today!

So, if you ever thought about making something that doesn't yet exist, start reading! In many years from today, who knows what you will end up with?

PHRASES FOR CHARTING

missed the intrusion

people will giggle

raffle away prizes

blocked their vision

need more prevention

always juggles with precision

buy the instructions

know the combination

the complex invention

admission to country

relax after concussion

the beautiful ocean

battle made trouble

scramble to assemble

more rapid confusion

always ruffle the crowd

1 DETERMINE SCORE

→ TOTAL WORDS READ	
− ERRORS	
= WORDS READ CORRECTLY	

2 CHART PROGRESS

GRAPH YOUR SCORE ON THE "MY PROGRESS" CHART FOR THIS UNIT

Student Name: _____   *Unit#* _____   *Test Date:* _____

SOUNDS

1 _____   2 _____   3 _____

WORDS

1 _____   6 _____

2 _____   7 _____

3 _____   8 _____

4 _____   9 _____

5 _____   10 _____

PHRASES

1 _____   3 _____

2 _____   4 _____

SENTENCES

1 _____

_____

2 _____

_____

UNIT SCORES

SOUNDS _____ /3   MARKING _____ /2 (❏ All elements of task 1 ❏ All elements of task 2)

PHONETIC WORDS _____ /20   CAPITALIZATION _____ /2 (❏ Sentence 1 ❏ Sentence 2)

HIGH FREQUENCY WORDS _____ /10   PUNCTUATION _____ /2 (❏ Sentence 1 ❏ Sentence 2)

LEGIBILITY _____ /1 (❏ All writing is legible)

THIS PAGE IS INTENTIONALLY LEFT BLANK

WILSON® Just Words®

Name _____

1. _____
2. _____
3. _____
4. _____
5. _____
6. _____
7. _____
8. _____
9. _____
10. _____
11. _____
12. _____
13. _____
14. _____
15. _____

HF Words = _____ / 15
+ Phonetic Words = _____ / 15
Total = _____ / 30

1. (every) profile
2. (pretty) and nifty
3. seventy (minutes)
4. (many) thorns
5. (people) are remarking
6. bombarded by (work)
7. display (beautiful) things
8. (about) his employment
9. discounted (right)
10. (great) laundry pile
11. (only) a thimble
12. (another) regulation
13. a (great) intrusion
14. (know) it was refundable
15. it was raffled (high)

Determine the correct word choice for the structure.

chase stove	ch a s e v-e	beagle table	d -le
plateful hopeful	v-e	treating screamed	d
athlete cupcake	c v-e	bleaches storms	d
decline complete	o v-e	nailed farming	r
duty ugly	c o	blurting steamer	r
choppy empty	c o	charm storm	r
sly shy	o	marble bugle	r -le
hotel pretend	o c	chains speaker	d
provide polite	o v-e	jockey lucky	c d
lady upon	o o	bellboy parsley	r d

Add suffixes to basewords below. Use spelling rules as needed.

drizzle + ing   =   <u>drizzling</u>

remark + able   =   _____

ban + ed   =   _____

formulate + ing =   _____

master + ed   =   _____

spin + er   =   _____

plenty + ful   =   _____

settle + ment   =   _____

lucky + est   =   _____

depend + able =   _____

stir + ing   =   _____

flat + ly   =   _____

cry + ed   =   <u>cried</u>

raffle + ed   =   _____

swerve + ing   =   _____

consider + able =   _____

puzzle + ed   =   _____

quote + able   =   _____

flag + ed   =   _____

interfere + ed   =   _____

boy + ish   =   _____

wag + ed   =   _____

involve + ment   =   _____

study + ed   =   _____

PHRASE PRACTICE

near the **conflict**

until this **invention**

should **permit** it

publish more work

continue to **enjoy**

disturbed them again

near another **galaxy**

is very **complex**

until the new **document**

decline in a minute

---

persistent this minute

until **teachers** confirm

does **blur** together

near another **nerve**

until you **comprehend**

large **harsh** mountain

dispute many topics

in a **partnership** again

near the **victim**

change the **container**

MARK UP BOLD WORDS

"Scoop" and mark syllables.

cŏnflĭct
c   c

PHRASE PRACTICE

usually the **safest**

always **involving** more

made the **littlest** changes

over rough **pavement**

usually trouble **intervening**

because mother was **stunned**

trotting through rough land

about **fixing** problems

sliding up and around

stirred every hour

---

happily change another

fixed right away

rallies around the country

usually more **soggy**

trouble **identifying** four

scarred around my elbow

struggling through rough times

drizzling has stopped

because it was **absolute**

raffled a great prize

MARK UP BOLD WORDS

Underline baseword and circle suffix. Indicate spelling rule as appropriate.

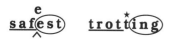

The Great Grizzly

The grizzly bear is a remarkable animal that is found in Canada, Alaska and some northern United States. Its color is varied and can be brown to nearly black with fur that seems to be white-tipped or frosted. That is why it is sometimes called the Silvertip Bear. This great mammal has a distinctive hump on its back and long, curved claws. Males can reach ten or even twelve feet tall on their hind legs! They can also grow to be four hundred to six hundred pounds although males have occasionally reached eight hundred pounds. Despite this impressive size, the grizzly can run at a speed of thirty or more miles per hour.

The grizzly bear eats both plants and animals, and in coastal places, it feasts on fish such as trout, bass and salmon. This powerful predator tends to be a solitary animal, but can be seen gathering by the dozen around great fishing spots. Grizzlies have been known to steal food which has led to some conflict with humans. In preparation for winter months, the bear gains fat by eating thousands of calories each day. Then, throughout the hardship of winter, the bear stays in a den at a high elevation for a deep sleep called hibernation. Some people dispute the hibernation of the grizzly and say if the bear lives where there is no lack of food, it may not hibernate at all.

I am sure that you would be absolutely thrilled to see this bear in the wild, but it mostly lives in remote forests that are undisturbed by humans. Although grizzly bears normally avoid contact with people, they can be aggressive. You could be risking your life if you are not attentive to your surroundings when you are hiking or camping in places that are home to these bears. If you do observe a grizzly in the wild, it is not an option to go near it, as any surprise intrusion could cause it to attack.

The number of grizzly bears rapidly declined in the United States because they were widely hunted and trapped before regulations were put into place. Thus, their population dwindled. Now with protection, hopefully they will find safe and plentiful habitats that will help them to thrive once again.

PHRASES FOR CHARTING

enjoying every minute

revolves around Earth

locating both athletes

acts extremely childish

throwing one blanket

near rough pavement

the littlest confusion

all blurring together

move shanty quarters

is always dependable

usually the flawless option

sprinkler spins around

authored the bound work

change is disruptive

happily on mission

baffled people again

1 DETERMINE SCORE

→	TOTAL WORDS READ	
−	ERRORS	
=	WORDS READ CORRECTLY	

2 CHART PROGRESS

GRAPH YOUR SCORE ON THE "MY PROGRESS" CHART FOR THIS UNIT

Student Name: _____ *Unit#* _____ *Test Date:* _____

SOUNDS

1 _____ 2 _____ 3 _____

WORDS

1 _____ 6 _____

2 _____ 7 _____

3 _____ 8 _____

4 _____ 9 _____

5 _____ 10 _____

PHRASES

1 _____ 3 _____

2 _____ 4 _____

SENTENCES

1 _____

_____

2 _____

_____

UNIT SCORES

SOUNDS	_____ /3	MARKING _____ /2 (☐ All elements of task 1 ☐ All elements of task 2)
PHONETIC WORDS	_____ /20	CAPITALIZATION _____ /2 (☐ Sentence 1 ☐ Sentence 2)
HIGH FREQUENCY WORDS	_____ /10	PUNCTUATION _____ /2 (☐ Sentence 1 ☐ Sentence 2)
		LEGIBILITY _____ /1 (☐ All writing is legible)

THIS PAGE IS INTENTIONALLY LEFT BLANK

Name _____

1. _____

2. _____

3. _____

4. _____

5. _____

6. _____

7. _____

8. _____

9. _____

10. _____

11. _____

12. _____

13. _____

14. _____

15. _____

(HF Words)   = _____ / 15
 + Phonetic Words = _____ / 15
   Total   = _____ / 30

1. sly (new) plan

2. (pretty) ruby ring

3. reject (every) plan

4. push (very) hard

5. will (learn) twirling

6. get (another) partner

7. preferring the (work)

8. use (enough) paint

9. a (high) payment

10. (about) to destroy

11. (because) he spies

12. (buy) for protection

13. the (first) mission

14. (change) the document

15. (usually) impressive

End Progress Check

"Scoop" sentences into phrases for meaning. Read the sentence. Mark up the bold words.

Reading and step-by-step investigation **played** a key role in the **invention**.
                                                       d   c c

The men **planned** an expedition to the remote **rainforest**.

Dust from a **swirling windstorm** can **sting** and can be very harsh.

Norman Rockwell's **paintings portray** American life as it was many years ago.

Hopefully the **Grizzlies** will find safe and plentiful **habitats** that will help them to thrive.

Match the meaning and example to the prefix. Use your Student Notebook if needed.

Prefix	Meaning	Example
mis	wrongly, badly	misbehave
non	_____	_____
en	_____	_____
e	_____	_____
un	_____	_____
de	_____	_____
ex	_____	_____
re	_____	_____
dis	_____	_____
pro	_____	_____
pre	_____	_____
trans	_____	_____
il,im,in,ir	_____	_____

Meaning

from, down, away	for, forward
not, opposite of	not
not, opposite of	not
across, beyond	before
out of, away from	back, again
out of, away from	in, into
~~wrongly, badly~~	

Example

exit	~~misbehave~~
nonsense	disconnect
illegal	emit
transport	recycle
unhappy	enlist
decrease	propel
predict	

Student Name: _____   *Test Date:* _____

SOUNDS

1 _____   2 _____   3 _____

WORDS

1 _____   6 _____

2 _____   7 _____

3 _____   8 _____

4 _____   9 _____

5 _____   10 _____

PHRASES

1 _____   3 _____

2 _____   4 _____

SENTENCES

1 _____

_____

2 _____

_____

UNIT SCORES

SOUNDS	_____ /3	MARKING	_____ /2 (❑ All elements of task 1 ❑ All elements of task 2)
PHONETIC WORDS	_____ /20	CAPITALIZATION	_____ /2 (❑ Sentence 1 ❑ Sentence 2)
HIGH FREQUENCY WORDS	_____ /10	PUNCTUATION	_____ /2 (❑ Sentence 1 ❑ Sentence 2)
		LEGIBILITY	_____ /1 (❑ All writing is legible)

Add suffixes to basewords below. Use spelling rules as needed. **(20 points)**

---

depend + able   =   _dependable_

portray + ing   =   _____   stir + ed   =   _____

puzzle + ing   =   _____   happy + ly   =   _____

care + ful   =   _____   observe + ing =   _____

intervene + ing =   _____   stun + ed   =   _____

rally + es   =   _____   settle + ment =   _____

Make the following words plural. **(20 points)**

---

donkey   =   _donkeys_

box   =   _____   porcupine =   _____

jersey   =   _____   nerve   =   _____

document   =   _____   porch   =   _____

marble   =   _____   galaxy   =   _____

daisy   =   _____   lobby   =   _____

Underline or "scoop" into syllables. Mark the syllables. **(30 points)**

ĕxplōsion   extensive   drowsy   unstable
 c o

relaxation   withdraw   admission   formulate

cheekbone   sparkle   harmonize   asteroid

Select the correct prefix. **(10 points)**

Prefix:

ex	trans	non	en	e	dis
~~pre~~	pro	de	en	mis	re

pre election
(before)

____honest (not) ____behave (wrongly) ____unite (again) ____effective (not) ____continental (across)

____equality (for) ____croach (near) ____escalate (down) ____rupt (out of) ____terminate (away from)

Match the meaning and example with the root. **(20 points)**

Root	Meaning	Example
fid	trust	confident
cred		
rupt		
fect		
sect		
dict		
sist		
strict		
flex		
tract		
min		

Meaning

speak	break
bend	make
cut	small, little
~~trust~~	make tight
to make firm, to stay	drag, pull
believe	

Example

miniature	flexible
constrict	infect
dictate	tractor
~~confident~~	credible
disrupt	dissect
insist	

PROGRESS CHECK: CHART HIGH FREQUENCY WORDS

Number of High Frequency Words Correct		2	3	4	5	6	7	midterm
	15	·	·	·	·	·	·	·
	14	·	·	·	·	·	·	●
	13	·	·	·	·	·	·	·
	12	·	·	·	·	·	·	·
	11	·	·	·	·	·	·	·
	10	·	·	·	·	·	·	·
	9	·	·	·	·	·	·	·
	8	·	·	·	·	·	·	·
	7	·	·	·	·	·	·	·
	6	·	·	·	·	·	·	·
	5	·	·	·	·	·	·	·
	4	·	·	·	·	·	·	·
	3	·	·	·	·	·	·	·
	2	·	·	·	·	·	·	·
	1	·	·	·	·	·	·	·
Unit ➜		2	3	4	5	6	7	midterm

PROGRESS CHECK: CHART PHONETIC WORDS

Number of Phonetic Words Correct		2	3	4	5	6	7	midterm
	15	·	·	·	·	·	·	·
	14	·	·	·	·	·	·	●
	13	·	·	·	·	·	·	·
	12	·	·	·	·	·	·	·
	11	·	·	·	·	·	·	·
	10	·	·	·	·	·	·	·
	9	·	·	·	·	·	·	·
	8	·	·	·	·	·	·	·
	7	·	·	·	·	·	·	·
	6	·	·	·	·	·	·	·
	5	·	·	·	·	·	·	·
	4	·	·	·	·	·	·	·
	3	·	·	·	·	·	·	·
	2	·	·	·	·	·	·	·
	1	·	·	·	·	·	·	·
Unit ➜		2	3	4	5	6	7	midterm

PROGRESS CHECK: CHART TOTAL (HIGH FREQUENCY AND PHONETIC WORDS)

Number of High Frequency Words and Phonetic Words Correct								
30	·	·	·	·	·	·	·	
29	·	·	·	·	·	·	·	
28	·	·	·	·	·	·	●	
27	·	·	·	·	·	·	·	
26	·	·	·	·	·	·	·	
25	·	·	·	·	·	·	·	
24	·	·	·	·	·	·	·	
23	·	·	·	·	·	·	·	
22	·	·	·	·	·	·	·	
21	·	·	·	·	·	·	·	
20	·	·	·	·	·	·	·	
19	·	·	·	·	·	·	·	
18	·	·	·	·	·	·	·	
17	·	·	·	·	·	·	·	
16	·	·	·	·	·	·	·	
15	·	·	·	·	·	·	·	
14	·	·	·	·	·	·	·	
13	·	·	·	·	·	·	·	
12	·	·	·	·	·	·	·	
11	·	·	·	·	·	·	·	
10	·	·	·	·	·	·	·	
9	·	·	·	·	·	·	·	
8	·	·	·	·	·	·	·	
7	·	·	·	·	·	·	·	
6	·	·	·	·	·	·	·	
5	·	·	·	·	·	·	·	
4	·	·	·	·	·	·	·	
3	·	·	·	·	·	·	·	
2	·	·	·	·	·	·	·	
1	·	·	·	·	·	·	·	
Unit ➜	2	3	4	5	6	7	midterm

My Progress

PROGRESS CHECK: CHART HIGH FREQUENCY WORDS

Number of High Frequency Words Correct								
15	·	·	·	·	·	·	·	·
14	·	·	·	·	·	·	·	●
13	·	·	·	·	·	·	·	·
12	·	·	·	·	·	·	·	·
11	·	·	·	·	·	·	·	·
10	·	·	·	·	·	·	·	·
9	·	·	·	·	·	·	·	·
8	·	·	·	·	·	·	·	·
7	·	·	·	·	·	·	·	·
6	·	·	·	·	·	·	·	·
5	·	·	·	·	·	·	·	·
4	·	·	·	·	·	·	·	·
3	·	·	·	·	·	·	·	·
2	·	·	·	·	·	·	·	·
1	·	·	·	·	·	·	·	·
Unit ➜	8	9	10	11	12	13	14	end

PROGRESS CHECK: CHART PHONETIC WORDS

Number of Phonetic Words Correct								
15	·	·	·	·	·	·	·	·
14	·	·	·	·	·	·	·	●
13	·	·	·	·	·	·	·	·
12	·	·	·	·	·	·	·	·
11	·	·	·	·	·	·	·	·
10	·	·	·	·	·	·	·	·
9	·	·	·	·	·	·	·	·
8	·	·	·	·	·	·	·	·
7	·	·	·	·	·	·	·	·
6	·	·	·	·	·	·	·	·
5	·	·	·	·	·	·	·	·
4	·	·	·	·	·	·	·	·
3	·	·	·	·	·	·	·	·
2	·	·	·	·	·	·	·	·
1	·	·	·	·	·	·	·	·
Unit ➜	8	9	10	11	12	13	14	end

PROGRESS CHECK: CHART TOTAL (HIGH FREQUENCY AND PHONETIC WORDS)

Number of High Frequency Words and Phonetic Words Correct	8	9	10	11	12	13	14	end
30	·	·	·	·	·	·	·	·
29	·	·	·	·	·	·	·	·
28	·	·	·	·	·	·	·	●
27	·	·	·	·	·	·	·	·
26	·	·	·	·	·	·	·	·
25	·	·	·	·	·	·	·	·
24	·	·	·	·	·	·	·	·
23	·	·	·	·	·	·	·	·
22	·	·	·	·	·	·	·	·
21	·	·	·	·	·	·	·	·
20	·	·	·	·	·	·	·	·
19	·	·	·	·	·	·	·	·
18	·	·	·	·	·	·	·	·
17	·	·	·	·	·	·	·	·
16	·	·	·	·	·	·	·	·
15	·	·	·	·	·	·	·	·
14	·	·	·	·	·	·	·	·
13	·	·	·	·	·	·	·	·
12	·	·	·	·	·	·	·	·
11	·	·	·	·	·	·	·	·
10	·	·	·	·	·	·	·	·
9	·	·	·	·	·	·	·	·
8	·	·	·	·	·	·	·	·
7	·	·	·	·	·	·	·	·
6	·	·	·	·	·	·	·	·
5	·	·	·	·	·	·	·	·
4	·	·	·	·	·	·	·	·
3	·	·	·	·	·	·	·	·
2	·	·	·	·	·	·	·	·
1	·	·	·	·	·	·	·	·
Unit ➜	8	9	10	11	12	13	14	end

My Progress

CHART UNIT PROGRESS

Unit: 1

Date:

Comments:

Phrases for Charting

5	10	15	20	25	30	35	40	45	50

Unit Test

Unit Test Scoring

										# correct		Total
Sounds	1	2	3								× 1 =	
Phonetic Words	1	2	3	4	5	6	7	8	9	10	11	12	13	14	15	16	17	18	19	20		× 3 =	
High Frequency Words	1	2	3	4	5	6	7	8	9	10		× 3 =	
Other	Marking 1 2	Capitalization 1 2	Punctuation 1 2	Legibility 1	× 1 =	

Total Score

Completed Assignments

☐ Homework ☐ Student Notebook ☐ Student Challenge

Unit: 2

Date:

Comments:

Phrases for Charting

5	10	15	20	25	30	35	40	45	50

Unit Test

Unit Test Scoring

										# correct		Total
Sounds	1	2	3								× 1 =	
Phonetic Words	1	2	3	4	5	6	7	8	9	10	11	12	13	14	15	16	17	18	19	20		× 3 =	
High Frequency Words	1	2	3	4	5	6	7	8	9	10		× 3 =	
Other	Marking 1 2	Capitalization 1 2	Punctuation 1 2	Legibility 1	× 1 =	

Total Score

Completed Assignments

☐ Homework ☐ Student Notebook ☐ Student Challenge

Unit: 3

Date:

Comments:

Phrases for Charting

	5	10	15	20	25	30	35	40	45	50

Unit Test

												Unit Test Scoring		
												# correct		Total
Sounds	1	2	3									x 1 =		
Phonetic Words	1	2	3	4	5	6	7	8	9	10	11	12	13	14	15	16	17	18	19	20	x 3 =
High Frequency Words	1	2	3	4	5	6	7	8	9	10		x 3 =		
Other	Marking	1	2	Capitalization	1	2	Punctuation	1	2	Legibility	1	x 1 =		

Total Score

Completed Assignments

☐ Homework　　☐ Student Notebook　　☐ Student Challenge

Unit: 4

Date:

Comments:

Phrases for Charting

	5	10	15	20	25	30	35	40	45	50

Unit Test

												Unit Test Scoring		
												# correct		Total
Sounds	1	2	3									x 1 =		
Phonetic Words	1	2	3	4	5	6	7	8	9	10	11	12	13	14	15	16	17	18	19	20	x 3 =
High Frequency Words	1	2	3	4	5	6	7	8	9	10		x 3 =		
Other	Marking	1	2	Capitalization	1	2	Punctuation	1	2	Legibility	1	x 1 =		

Total Score

Completed Assignments

☐ Homework　　☐ Student Notebook　　☐ Student Challenge

My Progress

Unit: 5

Date:

Comments:

Phrases for Charting

5	10	15	20	25	30	35	40	45	50

Unit Test

																				Unit Test Scoring	
																				# correct	Total
Sounds	1	2	3																	x 1 =	
Phonetic Words	1	2	3	4	5	6	7	8	9	10	11	12	13	14	15	16	17	18	19	20	x 3 =
High Frequency Words	1	2	3	4	5	6	7	8	9	10											x 3 =
Other	Marking	1	2	Capitalization	1	2	Punctuation	1	2	Legibility	1										x 1 =

Total Score

Completed Assignments

☐ Homework   ☐ Student Notebook   ☐ Student Challenge

Unit: 6

Date:

Comments:

Phrases for Charting

5	10	15	20	25	30	35	40	45	50

Unit Test

																				Unit Test Scoring	
																				# correct	Total
Sounds	1	2	3																	x 1 =	
Phonetic Words	1	2	3	4	5	6	7	8	9	10	11	12	13	14	15	16	17	18	19	20	x 3 =
High Frequency Words	1	2	3	4	5	6	7	8	9	10											x 3 =
Other	Marking	1	2	Capitalization	1	2	Punctuation	1	2	Legibility	1										x 1 =

Total Score

Completed Assignments

☐ Homework   ☐ Student Notebook   ☐ Student Challenge

Unit: 7

Date:

Comments:

Phrases for Charting

	5		10		15		20		25		30		35		40		45		50

Unit Test

Sounds	1	2	3																	
Phonetic Words	1	2	3	4	5	6	7	8	9	10	11	12	13	14	15	16	17	18	19	20
High Frequency Words	1	2	3	4	5	6	7	8	9	10										
Other	Marking	1	2	Capitalization	1	2	Punctuation	1	2	Legibility	1	

Unit Test Scoring

	# correct		Total
Sounds		x 1 =	
Phonetic Words		x 3 =	
High Frequency Words		x 3 =	
Other		x 1 =	
Total Score			

Completed Assignments

☐ Homework   ☐ Student Notebook   ☐ Student Challenge

My Progress

Midterm Exam

Date: **Comments:**

Part I

																				# correct	Total
Sounds	1	2	3																		
Phonetic Words	1	2	3	4	5	6	7	8	9	10	11	12	13	14	15	16	17	18	19	20	x 1 =
High Frequency Words	1	2	3	4	5	6	7	8	9	10											x 3 =
Other	Marking 1	2	Capitalization 1	2	Punctuation 1	2	Legibility 1														x 3 =
																					x 1 =

Total Score Part I

Part II

																					Total
Nonsense Word Marking	1	2	3	4	5	6	7	8	9	10	11	12	13	14	15	16	17	18	19	20	
Multisyllabic Word Marking	21	22	23	24	25	26	27	28	29	30	31	32	33	34	35	36	37	38	39	40	
Spelling /k/ Sound	1	2	3	4	5	6	7	8	9	10											
Adding Suffixes	1	2	3	4	5	6	7	8	9	10											
Matching Prefixes and Roots	1	2	3	4	5	6	7	8	9	10 (meaning)											
	1	2	3	4	5	6	7	8	9	10 (indicate prefix or root)											

Total Score Part II

Unit: 8

Comments:

Date:

Phrases for Charting

5	10	15	20	25	30	35	40	45	50

Unit Test

					Unit Test Scoring		
					# correct		Total
Sounds	1	2	3				
Phonetic Words	1 2 3 4 5 6 7 8 9 10 11 12 13 14 15 16 17 18 19 20				___	× 1 =	___
High Frequency Words	1 2 3 4 5 6 7 8 9 10				___	× 3 =	___
Other	Marking 1 2	Capitalization 1 2	Punctuation 1 2	Legibility 1	___	× 3 =	___
					___	× 1 =	___

Total Score ___

Completed Assignments

☐ Homework ☐ Student Notebook ☐ Student Challenge

Unit: 9

Comments:

Date:

Phrases for Charting

5	10	15	20	25	30	35	40	45	50

Unit Test

					Unit Test Scoring		
					# correct		Total
Sounds	1	2	3				
Phonetic Words	1 2 3 4 5 6 7 8 9 10 11 12 13 14 15 16 17 18 19 20				___	× 1 =	___
High Frequency Words	1 2 3 4 5 6 7 8 9 10				___	× 3 =	___
Other	Marking 1 2	Capitalization 1 2	Punctuation 1 2	Legibility 1	___	× 3 =	___
					___	× 1 =	___

Total Score ___

Completed Assignments

☐ Homework ☐ Student Notebook ☐ Student Challenge

My Progress

Unit: 10

Date:

Comments:

Phrases for Charting

	5	10	15	20	25	30	35	40	45	50

Unit Test

Sounds	1	2	3																	
Phonetic Words	1	2	3	4	5	6	7	8	9	10	11	12	13	14	15	16	17	18	19	20
High Frequency Words	1	2	3	4	5	6	7	8	9	10										
Other	Marking	1	2	Capitalization	1	2	Punctuation	1	2	Legibility	1

Unit Test Scoring

# correct		Total
	x 1	=
	x 3	=
	x 3	=
	x 1	=

Total Score

Completed Assignments ☐ Homework ☐ Student Notebook ☐ Student Challenge

---

Unit: 11

Date:

Comments:

Phrases for Charting

	5	10	15	20	25	30	35	40	45	50

Unit Test

Sounds	1	2	3																	
Phonetic Words	1	2	3	4	5	6	7	8	9	10	11	12	13	14	15	16	17	18	19	20
High Frequency Words	1	2	3	4	5	6	7	8	9	10										
Other	Marking	1	2	Capitalization	1	2	Punctuation	1	2	Legibility	1

Unit Test Scoring

# correct		Total
	x 1	=
	x 3	=
	x 3	=
	x 1	=

Total Score

Completed Assignments ☐ Homework ☐ Student Notebook ☐ Student Challenge

Unit: 12

Date:

Comments:

Phrases for Charting

	5	10	15	20	25	30	35	40	45	50

Unit Test

													Unit Test Scoring		
													# correct		Total
Sounds	1	2	3										x 1	=	
Phonetic Words	1	2	3	4	5	6	7	8	9	10	11	12	13	14	15	16	17	18	19	20	x 3	=	
High Frequency Words	1	2	3	4	5	6	7	8	9	10			x 3	=	
Other	Marking	1	2	Capitalization	1	2	Punctuation	1	2	Legibility	1	x 1	=	

Total Score

Completed Assignments

☐ Homework ☐ Student Notebook ☐ Student Challenge

Unit: 13

Date:

Comments:

Phrases for Charting

	5	10	15	20	25	30	35	40	45	50

Unit Test

													Unit Test Scoring		
													# correct		Total
Sounds	1	2	3										x 1	=	
Phonetic Words	1	2	3	4	5	6	7	8	9	10	11	12	13	14	15	16	17	18	19	20	x 3	=	
High Frequency Words	1	2	3	4	5	6	7	8	9	10			x 3	=	
Other	Marking	1	2	Capitalization	1	2	Punctuation	1	2	Legibility	1	x 1	=	

Total Score

Completed Assignments

☐ Homework ☐ Student Notebook ☐ Student Challenge

My Progress

Unit: 14

Date:

Comments:

Phrases for Charting

5	10	15	20	25	30	35	40	45	50

Unit Test

Sounds	1	2	3																
Phonetic Words	1	2	3	4	5	6	7	8	9	10	11	12	13	14	15	16	17	18	19	20
High Frequency Words	1	2	3	4	5	6	7	8	9	10
Other	Marking 1 2	Capitalization 1 2	Punctuation 1 2	Legibility 1

Unit Test Scoring

	# correct		Total
		x 1 =	
		x 3 =	
		x 3 =	
		x 1 =	
Total Score			

Completed Assignments

☐ Homework ☐ Student Notebook ☐ Student Challenge

Final Exam

Date:

Comments:

Part I

																				# correct	Total
Sounds	1	2	3																		
Phonetic Words	1	2	3	4	5	6	7	8	9	10	11	12	13	14	15	16	17	18	19	20	x 1 =
High Frequency Words	1	2	3	4	5	6	7	8	9	10											x 3 =
Other	Marking	1	2	Capitalization	1	2	Punctuation	1	2	Legibility	1										x 3 =
																					x 1 =

Total Score Part I

Part II

																															Total
Adding Suffixes	1	2	3	4	5	6	7	8	9	10	11	12	13	14	15	16	17	18	19	20											
Making Words Plural	1	2	3	4	5	6	7	8	9	10	11	12	13	14	15	16	17	18	19	20											
Multisyllabic Word Marking	1	2	3	4	5	6	7	8	9	10	11	12	13	14	15	16	17	18	19	20	21	22	23	24	25	26	27	28	29	30	
Identifying Prefixes	1	2	3	4	5	6	7	8	9	10	(meaning)																				
Matching Roots	1	2	3	4	5	6	7	8	9	10	(example)																				

Total Score Part II

My Progress

NOTES